Molecular Orbital Calculations

BOOKS BY JOHN D. ROBERTS

Basic Organic Chemistry, Part I

Nuclear Magnetic Resonance, Applications to Organic

Chemistry

An Introduction to the Analysis of Spin-Spin Splitting

in High-Resolution Nuclear Magnetic Resonance

Spectra

Notes

on

Molecular Orbital

Calculations

John D. Roberts

Professor of Organic Chemistry

California Institute of Technology

Illustrated by the Author

W. A. BENJAMIN, INC., NEW YORK, 1962

NOTES ON MOLECULAR ORBITAL CALCULATIONS

Manufactured in the United States of America
Library of Congress Catalog Card Number: 61-18159

First printing, September 1961
Second printing, with corrections, March 1962

The publisher wishes to express his appreciation
to Dr. Roberts, who, in addition to writing the
manuscript, prepared all the illustrations. The
author was also responsible for the editing and
composition; final pages, ready for the camera,
were typed at the California Institute of Technology under Dr. Roberts' supervision.

W. A. BENJAMIN, INC.
2465 BROADWAY, NEW YORK 25, NEW YORK

Preface

For practicing organic chemists the simple, linear-combination-of-atomic-orbitals (LCAO), molecular-orbital method permits useful calculations of semi-empirical electronic energies of unsaturated molecules with no more than high school algebra. Anyone who can find the roots of $x^4 - 5x^2 + 4x = 0$ graphically, analytically, or by successive substitutions can obtain the energy levels and calculate the π-electron energy of bicyclo[1.1.0]butadiene.

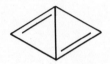

bicyclobutadiene

If in addition he can solve $x^4 - 4x^2 = 0$, then he can compare bicyclobutadiene with cyclobutadiene and predict what changes the 1,3 bond would make in the π-electron energies. With no more advanced mathematics, one can compute bond orders, charge distributions, and reactivity parameters for both free-radical and polar processes. The results may be crude, but they are often highly suggestive; there is no excuse for a modern organic chemist not to be able to use the LCAO method.

The notes that make up this book have been used for many years at the California Institute of Technology to introduce seniors and graduate students to the elements of the simple LCAO method. A fairly large number of exercises are interspersed in the text to illustrate important points. It is recommended that these be solved as encountered. Some of the problems are hoped to be suggestive of possible research problems in the field.

These Notes are not intended as a complete course of study and should be supplemented by the reference works listed in the Bibliography. No attempt has been made to survey the recent literature. The purpose has been to provide a practical introduction. As a result no appropriate acknowledgment to either the priority of ideas or to their development has been given.

This set of notes would never have been written without the generous contributions of Professor W. G. McMillan and Dr. V. Schomaker to the author's education in the subject matter. Camera copy was prepared by Mrs. Allene Luke with the aid of Miss Joy Matsumoto.

JOHN D. ROBERTS

Table of Contents

Preface. v

1. ATOMIC ORBITAL MODELS. 1

   Hydrogen-like Orbitals. 1

   Bond Formation Using Atomic Orbitals. 6

   Hybrid Bond Orbitals. 11

   Bond Orbitals for Atoms Carrying Unshared

      Electron Pairs. 14

   Orbitals for Multiple Bonds. 15

2. MOLECULAR ORBITAL CALCULATIONS. ELEC-
  TRONIC ENERGY LEVELS. 23

   The Wave Equation, ψ. 23

   Molecular Orbitals. The LCAO Method. 25

   The Overlap Integral, S_{ij}. 28

   The Coulomb Integral, α. 31

   The Resonance Integral, β. 32

   Energy Levels of $H_2^{\oplus}$. 33

   Bonding and Antibonding Orbitals. 36

   The Hydrogen Molecule. 39

   Localized Bonds. 40

   Ethylene by the LCAO Method. 42

   Butadiene, E_π. 43

   Butadiene Resonance Energy. 47

   The Butadiene Wave Functions. 48

3. BOND ORDERS, FREE-VALENCE INDEXES,
  AND CHARGE DISTRIBUTIONS. 53

   The Mobile Bond Order, p_{ij}. 53

   The Free-Valence Index, $\mathscr{F}_i$. 56

   Charge Distributions, q_i. 58

   Self-Consistent Fields. 59

4. APPLICATION OF GROUP THEORY TO
    SIMPLIFICATION OF MO DETERMINANTS 61
    The Butadiene Determinant 61
    Symmetry Operations 63
    Character Tables, D_{2v} 66
    The Trial Wave Function 67
    C_2 Symmetry 70
5. AROMATICITY. THE 4n + 2 RULE 73
    Cyclobutadiene by the LCAO Method 73
    The 4n + 2 Rule 75
6. MOLECULES WITH HETEROATOMS 77
7. NONPLANAR SYSTEMS 82
    Calculation of S_{ij} 82
    Nonplanar Intermediates 87
8. MOLECULAR ORBITAL THEORY AND CHEMICAL
    REACTIVITY 91
    The Reactivity Problem 91
    Predictions Based on the Ground State 94
    Perturbation Methods 95
    Localization Procedures 98
    Delocalization Procedures 100
    Product Stabilities 102
9. APPROXIMATE METHODS 105
    Nonbonding Molecular Orbitals 105
    Approximate Calculations of E_π 110
    Orientation in Aromatic Substitution 113
10. HIGHER-ORDER CALCULATIONS 115
Appendix I. SOLUTIONS OF TYPICAL EXERCISES IN
    THE USE OF THE LCAO METHOD 118

Exercise 2-8.............................118

Exercises 2-14, 3-1, 3-3 and 3-4 120

Appendix II. REPRINTS OF ARTICLES ON LCAO

CALCULATIONS.............................. 127

Appendix III. GENERAL BIBLIOGRAPHY.............. 140

Name Index.......................................142

Subject Index......................................145

Chapter 1

Atomic Orbital Models

MOLECULAR ORBITAL and valence bond calculations of the π-electron energies of unsaturated molecules customarily start with models in which appropriate atomic orbitals are assigned to each nucleus to provide a framework for motions of the binding electrons. Atomic orbital representations of organic molecules are now very commonly used in the teaching of elementary organic chemistry, although there often seems to be confusion between atomic orbital and molecular orbital representations.

Knowledge of how to set up an atomic orbital model for an organic molecule is crucial to the LCAO calculations described in these notes. Any reader who is familiar with atomic orbital representations can omit study of Chapter 1— or else only work the problems at the end of the chapter.

HYDROGEN-LIKE ORBITALS[1,2]

The quantum-mechanical treatment of the hydrogen atom has been thoroughly worked out. A number of stationary (non-time variable) states are possible. Each state may be

---

[1]Cf. C. A. Coulson, _Quarterly Reviews_, 1, 144 (1947).
[2]L. Pauling, "Nature of the Chemical Bond, " pp. 14-15, 32-37, 47-51, Cornell University Press, Ithaca, N. Y., 3rd Edition, 1960.

1

said to correspond to a particular atomic orbital. The wave-mechanical orbitals are quite different in concept from planetary orbits, and the position of the electron in a given orbital cannot be precisely defined. We can only speak of the probability of finding the electron within a given volume element at a given distance and direction from the nucleus.

The most stable state of the hydrogen atom is the 1s state where 1 refers to the principal quantum number as corresponds to the K shell for valence electrons. The 1s state is spherically symmetrical as regards to the probability density for the electron. As a function of radius, r, from the nucleus we have

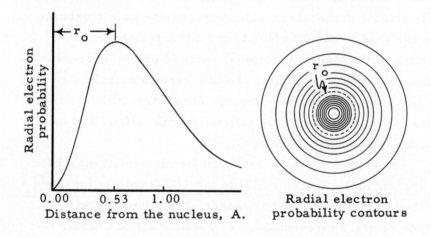

Radial electron probability

0.00   0.53   1.00
Distance from the nucleus, A.

Radial electron probability contours

where the radial probability is the probability of the electron being in the volume element defined by the distances r and r + dr. The distance of maximum probability r_o turns out to be just the distance taken as the normal radius of the electron orbit in the Bohr picture of the hydrogen atom.

We shall henceforth represent the 1s orbital as a spherical shell about the nucleus having a radius such that the probability of finding the electron within the boundary surface is high (0.8 to 0.95):

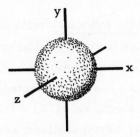

The 2s state is very much like the 1s state except that r_o is larger and the energy greater.

The 2p states (three in all) are quite different in geometrical form.

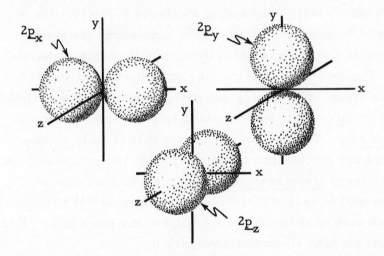

The axes of the three p orbitals lie at right angles to one another, and the orbitals are not spherically symmetrical about the nucleus.

The 3s and 3p states are similar to the 2s and 2p states but are of higher energy. The 3d, 4f, etc. orbitals have still higher energies and quite different geometries. Generally, the 3d and 4f orbitals are not important for bonding in most organic substances, at least those which are compounds of hydrogen and elements in the first long row of the periodic table.

4

The Pauli exclusion principle tells us that no more than two electrons can occupy a given orbital and then only if they do not have identical quantum numbers. Two electrons in the same orbital differ with respect to electron spin, which has the permitted quantum numbers +1/2, -1/2. Two electrons with "paired" spins may be symbolized as ↑↓ . Such a pair of electrons can go into a single orbital. The symbols ↑↑ (or ↓↓) represent two electrons that may not go together into a single orbital.

If we assume that all atomic nuclei have orbitals like those of the hydrogen atom,* we can see how more complex atoms can be built up by adding electrons to the orbitals in order of decreasing stability. For each atom, the proper number of electrons is added to balance the nuclear charge.

Figure 1 shows the building up of the lowest state of a carbon atom. The two highest energy electrons are put into different 2p orbitals with unpaired spins in accordance with Hund's rule. The rationale of Hund's rule is quite simple. If there are two electrons that can go into two orbitals of the same energy (degenerate orbitals), their mutual repulsion energy will be less if they have unpaired spins (↑↑) and thus are not able to be in the same orbital at the same time. For this reason, the electronic configuration

is expected to be more stable than the configuration

if the orbitals have the same energy.

*With the hydrogen atom, the 2s and 2p states have the same energy (accidental degeneracy). Since this is not true for other atoms, we shall show 2s and 2p states as having different energies.

$4\underline{p}$ ◯ Se/Ga   ◯ Br/Ge   ◯ Kr/As

$4\underline{s}$ ◯ Ca/K $3\underline{d}$ ◯ Fe/Sc   ◯ Co/Ti   ◯ Ni/V   ◯ Cu/Cr   ◯ Zn/Mn

$3\underline{p}$ ◯ S/Al   ◯ Cl/Si   ◯ A/P

$3\underline{s}$ ◯ Mg/Na

$2\underline{p}$ (↑) O/B   (↑) F/C   ◯ Ne/N

$2\underline{s}$ (↑↓) Be/Li

$1\underline{s}$ (↑↓) He/H

Fig. 1. — Atomic energy levels

States like the one shown in Fig. 1 for carbon are built up through the following steps. Helium has two paired electrons in the $1\underline{s}$ orbital; its configuration is written $1\underline{s}^2$.

$$He^{++} + 2e(\downarrow\uparrow) \longrightarrow He \quad 1\underline{s}^2 \text{ (more stable state than } 1\underline{s}2\underline{s}; \ 1\underline{s}2\underline{p}, \text{ etc.)}$$

$$He^{++} + 2e(\uparrow\uparrow) \begin{cases} \longrightarrow\!\!\!/\!\!\!\longrightarrow He \quad 1\underline{s}^2 \\ \longrightarrow He \quad 1\underline{s}2\underline{s} \text{ (most stable state possible for helium with unpaired electrons)} \end{cases}$$

For $Li^{+++} + 3e$, we expect $Li \ 1\underline{s}^2 2\underline{s}$ as the stable state where the $1\underline{s}^2$ electrons are paired. Continuing in this way we can derive the electronic configurations for the elements in the

6

first two rows of the periodic table as shown in Table 1-1.
These configurations follow Hund's rule for the most stable
electron state.

BOND FORMATION USING ATOMIC ORBITALS

In writing the conventional Lewis structures for molecules, we assume that a covalent chemical bond between two
atoms involves sharing of a pair of electrons from each atom.
The following representation shows how atomic orbitals can
be considered to be used in bond formation.

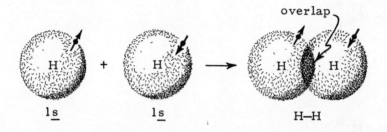

Here, we postulate that: Single bonds are formed by the pull-
ing together of atomic nuclei through attractive forces exerted
by electrons having paired spins (↑↓) in overlapping orbitals.
This formulation is no particular improvement over what is
implied by Lewis structures, except in so far as it provides
further appreciation that the electrons involved must have
paired spins. Because only two paired electrons can occupy
a given orbital, a clear reason is provided as to why two
electrons are involved in single-bond formation rather than
3, 5 or 10. This type of bond is called, in molecular-orbital
parlance, a σ bond.

An important idea which is not clearly (if at all) implied
in Lewis structures is: The direction of a bond will be such
as to have the orbitals of the bonding electrons overlap as
much as possible for a given internuclear distance.

Table 1-1

Electronic Configurations of Ground States of Atoms

H	Be	B	C	N	O
$1s$	$1s^2 2s^2$	$1s^2 2s^2 2p$	$1s^2 2s^2 2p^2$	$1s^2 2s^2 2p^3$	$1s^2 2s^2 2p^4$

	He
	$1s^2$

F	Ne
$1s^2 2s^2 2p^5$	$1s^2 2s^2 2p^6$

Li	Na
$1s^2 2s$	$1s^2 2s^2 2p^6 3s$

Mg	Al	Si	P	S	Cl	A
$\cdots 3s^2$	$\cdots 3s^2 3p$	$\cdots 3s^2 3p^2$	$\cdots 3s^2 3p^3$	$\cdots 3s^2 3p^4$	$\cdots 3s^2 3p^5$	$\cdots 3s^2 3p^6$

This idea does not apply to bonds involving only s
orbitals because s orbitals are spherically symmetrical.
However, it is very important in the formation of bonds
with p orbitals. For bonding of a hydrogen by its 1s orbital

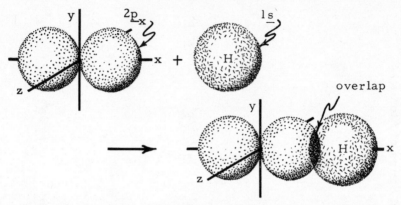

to a given p orbital, the hydrogen nucleus will lie along the
axis of the p orbital since this gives the maximum overlap
for a given degree of internuclear repulsion.

For an atom which forms two σ bonds with p orbitals
to hydrogen we would expect the $< H-X-H$ to be 90°.*

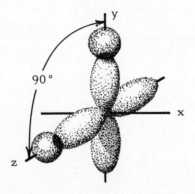

---

*In the drawings here and later the shapes of the p
orbitals will be represented as grossly elongated, tangent
ellipsoids instead of tangent spheres. This representation
is desirable in order to make the drawings clear and should
not be taken for the correct orbital shape.

The orbital treatment here offers improvement over Lewis structures through the idea of directed bonds and the possibility of predicting bond angles. Without further thought it would be possible to go too far and predict, because only s and p orbitals are commonly involved for the atoms of organic compounds of elements in the first long row of the periodic system, that all bond angles for such substances would be either indeterminate (s orbitals with spherical symmetry) or 90° (p orbitals). This dilemma has been resolved by orbital hybridization, as will be described later.

A useful working postulate is: The strongest bonds are formed when the overlapping of the orbitals is at a maximum. On this basis we expect differences in bond-forming power for s, p, d, and f orbitals since these orbitals have different radial distributions. The relative scales of extension for $2s$ and $2p$ orbitals are 1 and $\sqrt{3}$ respectively.

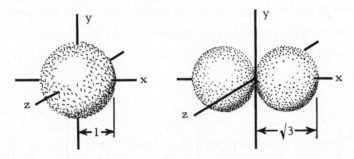

The shape of the p orbitals leads to the expectation that p orbitals should be able to overlap other orbitals better than s orbitals and hence that p bonds should be generally stronger than s bonds. If there is a choice between formation of s and p bonds, p bonds should lead to more stable compounds.

The distribution of p orbitals about the nucleus leads to the expectation that p bonds should be at right angles to one another. The water molecule might be formulated thus in terms of atomic orbitals:

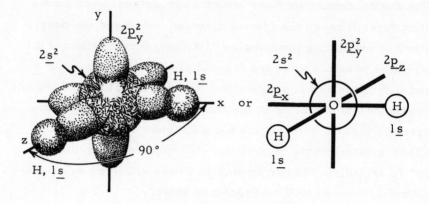

(It will be seen that the octet rule follows very naturally here through having all available stable orbitals filled with electrons.) The actual < H—O—H is 104.5°, which is quite a bit larger than the predicted value of 90°. One explanation of the difference between the found value and 90° is that electrostatic repulsions between the hydrogens (which must be partially positive because of the greater electron-attracting power of oxygen relative to hydrogen) tend to spread the H—O—H angle.[3]

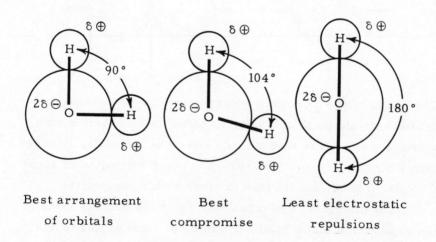

| Best arrangement of orbitals | Best compromise | Least electrostatic repulsions |

[3]Ref. 2, p. 111.

The 104.5° angle is then the best possible compromise between electrostatic repulsion and the bond weakening expected because of departure from the favorable 90° angle for p̲-orbital overlap.

Considerable support for this idea is provided by the < H–S–H of 92° in hydrogen sulfide, which, with a larger central atom and less ionic bonds, would have smaller electrostatic repulsions between the hydrogens than water.

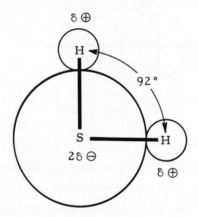

Significantly PH₃, AsH₃, and H₂Se all have < H–X–H = 90° ± 2°.

HYBRID BOND ORBITALS

From what has been said so far, one might expect carbon with the $1s^2 2s^2 2p^2$ configuration to form only compounds such as :CR₂ with < R–C–R = 90°, or else $1s^2 2sp^3$ compounds (CR₄) with three p̲ bonds at 90° to one another and an s̲ bond in an unspecified direction. Since CH₄, CCl₄, etc. have been shown beyond any possible doubt to have tetrahedral configurations, the simple orbital picture breaks down when applied to carbon.

Pauling and Slater have resolved this discrepancy between theory and experiment by introducing the concept

of orbital hybridization.[4] The hybridization procedure
involves determining which (if any) linear combinations of
s and p orbitals might make more effective bonds than the
individual s and p orbitals for a given total number of bonds.

By way of illustration let us suppose that we have a s
and a p orbital available to form two bonds:

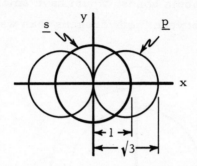

Note that neither the s or p orbitals can utilize all of their
overlapping potential for an s orbital of another nucleus along
the x axis. Obviously, however, if we can combine these
orbitals in such a way as to utilize more of the overlapping
power of the orbitals, we would have stronger bonds and more
stable molecules. It should be clear that mutual reinforce-
ment of the s and p_x orbitals will be expected to be most effective along the x axis. The mathematical treatment of
orbital hybridization is beyond the scope of these notes; however, the results are in accord with our expectation in that
two new orbitals are predicted. Each of these has an angular
dependence something like as shown on the following page with
overlapping power of 1.93 compared to the s orbital taken as
unity. Since these orbitals are a combination or a hybrid of
a s and a p orbital, they are commonly called "sp-hybrid
orbitals". Both lobes of the hybrid orbitals can be used for
bond formation, and bond angles of 180° are expected.

[4]Ref. 2, pp. 111-126.

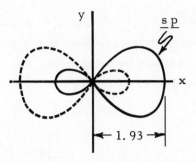

In agreement with these ideas, mercury in $(CH_3)_2Hg$ forms two covalent bonds and the $< C-Hg-C$ is $180°$. Similarly, $< C-Ag-C = 180°$ in the $[N\equiv C-Ag-C\equiv N^{\ominus}]$ complex.

For atoms forming three covalent bonds we expect $\underline{sp}^2$ hybridization:

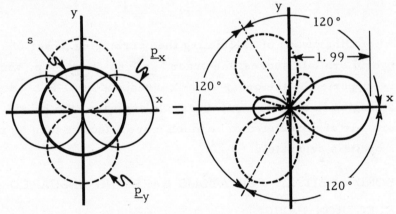

The $\underline{sp}^2$ orbitals have their axes in a common plane because the $\underline{p}$ orbitals are thereby utilized most effectively. The predicted overlapping power of these orbitals is 1.99.

On the assumption of formation of $\underline{sp}^2$-hybrid bonds, trivalent compounds of boron are expected to be planar with angles between bonds of $120°$. This geometry has been demonstrated for BCl_3, $B(CH_3)_3$, etc.

For $\underline{sp}^3$-hybrid orbitals of elements such as carbon, we will not expect the four hybrid orbitals to lie in one plane; actually, the axes of the best hybrid orbitals $(\underline{sp}^3)$ that can

be formed are predicted to be directed at angles of 109° 28'
to each other. These angles are just the tetrahedral angles
found for methane, carbon tetrachloride, etc. The predicted
relative overlapping power of $\underline{sp}^3$-hybrid orbitals is 2.00.

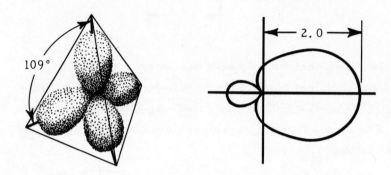

Other ways of calculating the overlapping power of
hybrid orbitals suggest the order[5] $\underline{sp} > \underline{sp}^2 > \underline{sp}^3 \gg \underline{p}$, which
is supported by the order of the corresponding C—H bond
strengths in organic compounds. In any case, the hybrid
orbitals are predicted to be much more effective than $\underline{p}$ or
$\underline{s}$ orbitals separately.

BOND ORBITALS FOR ATOMS CARRYING UNSHARED
ELECTRON PAIRS

Hybridization might be expected to be quite important
in ammonia, in water, and in similar compounds with unshared electron pairs because use of the 2$\underline{s}$ orbitals would
make stronger bonds, perhaps of the $\underline{sp}^3$ type, consequently
giving more stable molecules. But such hybridization does
not seem to be important. The reason is that in order to
use the $\underline{s}$ orbital for bond formation, an electron has to be
promoted from $\underline{s}^2$ to a higher orbital. Thus, if $\underline{sp}^2$ bonds

[5]C. A. Coulson, "Valence", pp. 198-200, Oxford
University Press, London, 1952.

are to be made and the unshared pair is put in $2\underline{p}^2$, then for nitrogen the following change is necessary:

$$\begin{array}{ccc} (\underline{p}) & & (\underline{p}^2) \\ & \overset{\textstyle\cdot}{} & \overset{\textstyle\cdot\cdot}{} \\ (\underline{p}) \quad \cdot\, N : \ (\underline{s}^2) & \longrightarrow & (\underline{p}) \quad \cdot\, N \, \cdot \quad (\underline{s}) \\ & \overset{\textstyle\cdot}{} & \overset{\textstyle\cdot}{} \\ (\underline{p}) & & (\underline{p}) \end{array}$$

The promotion energy for this change from $1\underline{s}^2 2\underline{s}^2 2\underline{p}^3$ to $1\underline{s}^2 2s 2\underline{p}^4$ is on the order of 200 kcal. for nitrogen.

Although changing from pure $\underline{p}$ to $\underline{sp}^2$ bonds might increase the bond strengths by as much as 25 to 30 kcal.,[4] this does not appear to be enough to compensate for promotion of the $\underline{s}$ electron. No important hybridization of the $\underline{s}$ and $\underline{p}$ orbitals is to be expected for compounds with unshared electron pairs, such as ammonia and water.

For atoms such as carbon, the $\underline{s}$- to $\underline{p}$-promotion energy is compensated for by the possibility of forming more bonds, not just better bonds. Thus $C(2\underline{s}^2 2\underline{p}_x 2\underline{p}_y)$ might form two $\underline{p}$ bonds of perhaps 80 kcal. each to hydrogen atoms and liberate 160 kcal., while $C(2s 2\underline{p}_x 2\underline{p}_y 2\underline{p}_z)$ could form four $\underline{sp}^3$ bonds of 103 kcal. each to hydrogen atoms and liberate 412 kcal. The energy of the latter process is clearly sufficient to accommodate the electron promotion energy (96 kcal.) for $C\ 1\underline{s}^2 2\underline{s}^2 2\underline{p}^2 \longrightarrow C\ 1\underline{s}^2 2s 2\underline{p}^3$, and promotion and hybridization with the formation of two extra strong bonds is to be expected.

ORBITALS FOR MULTIPLE BONDS

There are several possible atomic orbital formulations of multiple bonds.[6] For the LCAO treatment of unsaturated compounds, the so-called σ-π formulation of multiple bonds is most suited for practical calculations. This fact should

[6] Ref. 2, pp. 136-142.

not be taken as implying any real fundamental validity relative to other formulations. A σ–π formulation of nitrogen follows:

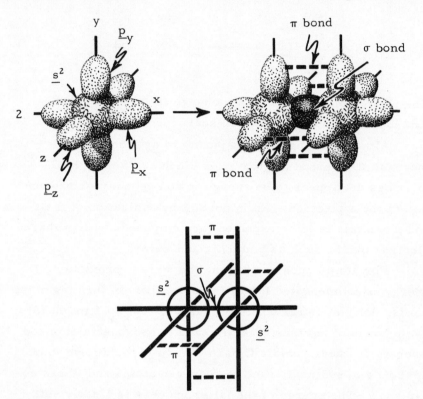

The sidewise overlapping of $\underline{p}$ orbitals is designated as π overlap to distinguish it from the endwise σ overlap.

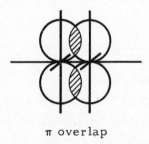

π overlap

The $\underline{s}$ electrons will not be significantly involved in the N–N triple bond because of the promotion energy of the $\underline{s}$ electrons.

For acetylene, the bonding is not well formulated with σ–type p bonds with the 2s orbitals filled as shown below:

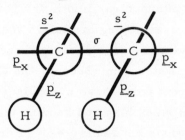

First, the —C≡C— bond is stronger (194 kcal.) than a —C–C— bond (83 kcal.); second, the H–C–C angles are not 90° but 180°. The following model is more reasonable:

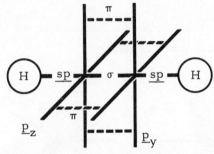

This structure fits well with the properties of acetylenic bonds in being linear with high refractivity (ease of interaction of light with electrons) and high chemical reactivity (π electrons exposed).

The question arises as to why acetylene is not just as well formulated with sp³ bonds.

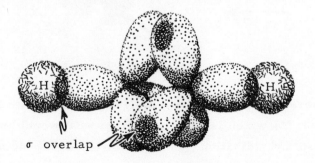

σ overlap

The following reasons may be advanced against such a formulation: First, sp^3 bonds are not expected to be very
favorable when the internuclear line is far from coinciding
with the axis of the overlapping orbitals. With sp^3 orbitals,
the bonds would have to be considerably "bent" bonds of
much less than usual strength. Second, the C—H bonds in
acetylene are different from those in ethylene or ethane, as
judged by their C—H stretching and bending frequencies in
the infrared and in their bond energies.[5] Furthermore, the
hydrogens of acetylene are very much more acidic than those
of ethane. If we conclude that the C—H bonds are not sp^3 in
character, then as a corollary the C—C bonds are not sp^3
either.

Ethylenic bonds may be formulated as follows with
atomic orbitals and σ—π bonding:

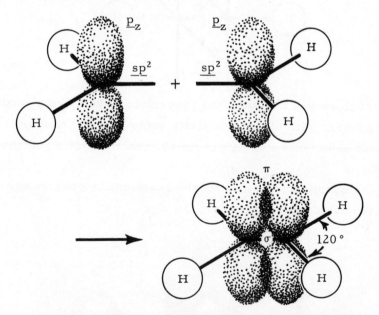

The observed values for the H—C—H angles of ethylene are
$116.7 \pm 0.7°$, which is rather far from what would be expected for sp^3 hybridization. In addition, the C—H bending and

stretching vibrations of ethylene in the infrared are different from those of acetylene and ethane. That the H—C—H angle of ethylene and the corresponding external angles of other alkenes range from 116.7° to close to 115° rather than the 120° predicted for pure sp^2 bonds may be regarded as significant or not, depending upon one's point of view. [6] For the purposes of the present discussion, we shall assume that the σ-π formulation is by no means rendered untenable by the existing evidence and that, in fact, it will be the formulation of choice for LCAO calculations.

On the basis of the σ-π model, we can conclude that the following twisted configuration should not be very stable:

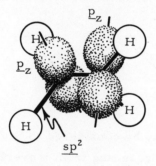

Here the p_z orbitals are not in position to overlap effectively in the π manner. The favored configuration is expected to have the axes of the p-π orbitals parallel; as a result all the atoms directly attached by sp^2-σ bonds to the ethylenic linkage should all lie in the same plane. This is, of course, in agreement with experiment. Since considerable energy would have to be put in to break the p-π double bond and to permit rotation about the remaining sp^2-σ bond, restricted rotation and stable cis-trans isomers are expected.

For a system with 1,3-double bonds, such as butadiene, we can make up an atomic orbital model as shown on the next page:

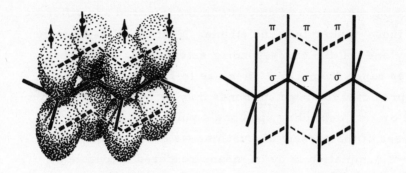

From this model we can expect behavior for butadiene which would not be possible in molecules with isolated double bonds because of the π overlap involving the 2, 3 orbitals. This can be expressed in more conventional symbols as

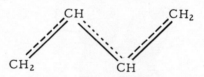

where the 2, 3 bond may be considered to have at least some double-bond character resulting from π overlap. We shall show later how the importance of 2, 3 bonding can be estimated for 1, 3-butadiene.

For benzene, we can construct the following atomic orbital model:

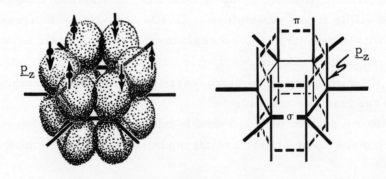

Each $\underline{p}_z$ electron is paired with its neighbor, and the
$\underline{p}$ orbitals overlap in the π manner around the ring. Note
that all of the π bonds are expected to be equivalent if the
C—C bond distances are equal. The atomic orbital picture
accounts well for the stability and symmetry of benzene. It
is somewhat less satisfactory in the particular form to explain the properties and reactions of substituted benzene
derivatives.

On extension of atomic orbital approaches to cycloöctatetraene, it is found impossible to construct an unstrained

planar model with $\underline{sp^2}$–σ bonds at 120°.
There is no unstrained atomic orbital
model where the $\underline{p}_z$ orbitals on one
carbon atom can overlap equally effectively with those on contiguous

Cyclooctatetraene   carbon atoms.

In this situation one might foresee either a strained
planar structure with strong π bonding such as in benzene or
an unstrained nonplanar structure with more or less isolated
double bonds. In any case, we do not expect cyclooctatetraene to behave like benzene. Actually cyclooctatetraene be-
haves like an unsaturated compound and possesses the "tub"
configuration with alternating single and double bonds as
shown below:

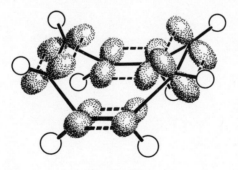

"tub"

Exercise 1-1

Make drawings of atomic orbital models for each of the following compounds. Each drawing should be large and clear with indication of the expected bond angles. Be sure that orbitals occupied by unshared pairs as well as those used by each atom in bond formation are correctly labeled.

a. F_2

b. H_2S

c. acetonitrile

d. phenanthrene

e. graphite

f. HCN

g. CO_2

h. H_2O_2

i. BF_3

j. $(CH_3)_2Mg$

k. CH_3NO_2

l. ketene

m. pyridine

n. diazomethane

($< C–N–N = 180°$)

o. methyl isocyanide

($< C–N–C = 180°$)

p. $CH_5^{\oplus}$

Chapter 2

Molecular Orbital Calculations. Electronic Energy Levels

IN THE APPLICATION of molecular orbital theory to calculations of chemical binding energies, we shall use several basic principles, some of which were mentioned in Chapter 1 and are given here by way of review:

1. Electrons may be assigned to definite orbitals. — Wave-mechanical orbitals differ fundamentally from the precisely defined orbits of the Bohr quantum theory. The electron cannot be located exactly in the orbital (uncertainty principle), and one can only calculate the probability that the electron will be present in a given volume element in the region of the nucleus.

2. An electron in a particular orbital may be assigned a definite energy.

3. Only two nonidentical electrons may occupy a given orbital. (See p. 4)

4. The forces involved in chemical binding are electrostatic in nature.

THE WAVE EQUATION, ψ

We shall start with an elementary and general introduction to the wave equation and become more specific and more approximate as required by the complexities to be encountered. First, we consider the $H_2^{\oplus}$ molecule ion because this is the simplest

of all bonded species with just two nuclei and one electron.
The energy of the system can be divided into potential and
kinetic energy as follows:

Total energy = potential energy + kinetic energy
$$E = P + K$$

If the system were to obey classical mechanics, then E = H,
where H represents the Hamiltonian for a stationary (time-
independent) state. For wave motion this equation is rewrit-
ten as

$$H\psi = E\psi$$

where ψ is the wave function and H is the Hamiltonian energy
operator.[1] We shall not be concerned with the precise mathematical form of either H or ψ. The following general remarks
can be made regarding H and ψ:

1. H contains both potential and kinetic energy terms.

2. $H\psi$ is to be taken as the result of the operation of
H on the function ψ just as $2x$ is the result of the operation of
d/dx on x^2. For this reason we expect $H\psi \neq \psi H$ even though
$E\psi = \psi E$.

3. ψ is an electron amplitude function that may have
either a positive or negative sign at a given point (x, y, z) and
has properties such that $\psi^2(x, y, z)\, dx\, dy\, dz$ is proportional to
the probability of finding the electron at (x, y, z) in a volume
element of size $dx\, dy\, dz$. Now, if

$$\int_{-\infty}^{\infty} \int_{-\infty}^{\infty} \int_{-\infty}^{\infty} \psi^2\, dx\, dy\, dz = 1 \ \left(\text{or} \int \psi^2\, d\tau = 1\right)$$

then the wave function ψ is said to be normalized. This
amounts to saying that there is unit probability of finding an

[1] C. A. Coulson, "Valence", Chap. III, Oxford University Press, London, 1952.

electron having the wave function ψ somewhere in all space. Strictly speaking, we should consider the possibility of complex ψ functions, i. e. those containing $\sqrt{-1}$; in such cases the normalized functions have

$$\int \psi \psi^* \, d\tau = 1$$

where ψ^* = the complex conjugate of ψ. But we shall ignore such possibilities because complex ψ functions will not be important in the type of calculations covered by these Notes.

4. Each state of the hydrogen atom, $1\underline{s}$, $2\underline{s}$, $2\underline{p}$, etc., has a corresponding ψ function[*] from which the electron probability density and energy can be calculated.

5. H will not contain time as a variable for the states that will be of interest to us here.

MOLECULAR ORBITALS. THE LCAO METHOD

The molecular orbital method assumes that the properties of $H_2^{\oplus}$ might be calculated through consideration of the two nuclei surrounded by a single molecular orbital represented by $\psi_{molecule}$ and containing one electron. Thus,

$$H\psi_{molecule} = E\psi_{molecule}$$

where $\int (\psi_{molecule})^2 \, d\tau = 1$, if $\psi_{molecule}$ is normalized. These equations are not formidable; the trouble comes in the form of H and $\psi_{molecule}$ and the use of them to calculate E.

The linear combination of atomic orbital (LCAO) method for $H_2^{\oplus}$ assumes that $\psi_{molecule}$ can be approximated

[*]A serious notational problem arises with regard to the atomic wave functions. Various authors have used ψ, ϕ, X, etc. We shall use X but with no conviction that this is the best or wisest choice.

as a linear combination of atomic orbitals having the individual wave functions X_n. Thus $\psi_{molecule} \sim c_1 X_1 + c_2 X_2$. The coefficients c_1 and c_2 might be expected to be equal for $H_2^{\oplus}$ but unequal for unsymmetrical molecules such as LiH. We shall find that the number of constructable molecular orbitals in the LCAO method is always equal to the number of atomic orbitals.

We shall treat c_1 and c_2 as parameters for which we shall wish to determine values; ψ will be used for $\psi_{molecule}$ and X_1 and X_2 will be used for the respective atomic orbitals. E will be found in terms of c_1 and c_2 and the energies of the atomic orbitals, and to do this we start with

$$H\psi = E\psi$$

and multiply through by ψ so that

$$\psi H\psi = E\psi^2$$

Integration over all space then gives

$$\int \psi H\psi \, d\tau = E \int \psi^2 \, d\tau$$

or

$$E = \frac{\int \psi H\psi \, d\tau}{\int \psi^2 \, d\tau}$$

In the last equation E is obtained in a form such that the coordinate problem is greatly simplified. Substituting $c_1 X_1 + c_2 X_2$ for ψ we have

$$E = \frac{\int (c_1 X_1 + c_2 X_2) \, H \, (c_1 X_1 + c_2 X_2) \, d\tau}{\int (c_1 X_1 + c_2 X_2)^2 \, d\tau}$$

$$= \frac{\int (c_1 X_1 H c_1 X_1 + c_1 X_1 H c_2 X_2 + c_2 X_2 H c_1 X_1 + c_2 X_2 H c_2 X_2) \, d\tau}{\int (c_1^2 X_1^2 + 2c_1 c_2 X_1 X_2 + c_2^2 X_2^2) \, d\tau}$$

It can be shown for solutions of E which correspond to physical reality that

$$\int X_1 H X_2 \, d\tau = \int X_2 H X_1 \, d\tau$$

We can now make the following substitutions:

$$H_{11} = \int X_1 H X_1 \, d\tau$$

$$H_{12} = H_{21} = \int X_1 H X_2 \, d\tau = \int X_2 H X_1 \, d\tau$$

$$H_{22} = \int X_2 H X_2 \, d\tau$$

$$S_{11} = \int X_1^2 \, d\tau$$

$$S_{12} = \int X_1 X_2 \, d\tau$$

$$S_{22} = \int X_2^2 \, d\tau$$

$$\therefore \ E = \frac{c_1^2 H_{11} + 2c_1 c_2 H_{12} + c_2^2 H_{22}}{c_1^2 S_{11} + 2c_1 c_2 S_{12} + c_2^2 S_{22}}$$

We are interested in the minimum value of the energy. Using the variation method,[1] we have

$$\frac{\partial E}{\partial c_1} = \frac{(c_1^2 S_{11} + 2c_1 c_2 S_{12} + c_2^2 S_{22})(2c_1 H_{11} + 2c_2 H_{12})}{(c_1^2 S_{11} + 2c_1 c_2 S_{12} + c_2^2 S_{22})^2}$$

$$- \frac{(c_1^2 H_{11} + 2c_1 c_2 H_{12} + c_2^2 H_{22})(2c_1 S_{11} + 2c_2 S_{12})}{(c_1^2 S_{11} + 2c_1 c_2 S_{12} + c_2^2 S_{22})^2} = 0$$

$$(2c_1 H_{11} + 2c_2 H_{12}) = \frac{c_1^2 H_{11} + 2c_1 c_2 H_{12} + c_2^2 H_{22}}{(c_1^2 S_{11} + 2c_1 c_2 S_{12} + c_2^2 S_{22})} (2c_1 S_{11} + 2c_2 S_{12})$$

and
$$c_1 H_{11} + c_2 H_{12} = E(c_1 S_{11} + c_2 S_{12})$$

or
$$c_1 (H_{11} - ES_{11}) + c_2 (H_{12} - ES_{12}) = 0$$

In the same way $\partial E / \partial c_2 = 0$ yields

$$c_1 (H_{12} - ES_{12}) + c_2 (H_{22} - ES_{22}) = 0$$

Permitted values of E for the system of simultaneous "secular" equations correspond to the roots of the secular determinant

$$\begin{vmatrix} H_{11} - ES_{11} & H_{12} - ES_{12} \\ H_{12} - ES_{12} & H_{22} - ES_{22} \end{vmatrix} = 0$$

Once we know E we can get ratios of c_1 and c_2 from the simultaneous equations. Final c_1 and c_2 values must conform to the normalization condition. In the general case, where $\psi = c_1 \psi_1 + c_2 \psi_2 + \cdots c_n \psi_n$, the "secular" determinant becomes

$$\begin{vmatrix} H_{11} - S_{11} E & H_{12} - S_{12}E \cdots H_{1n} - S_{1n}E \\ H_{12} - S_{12}E & H_{22} - S_{22}E \cdots H_{2n} - S_{2n}E \\ H_{13} - S_{13}E & H_{23} - S_{23}E \cdots H_{3n} - S_{3n}E \\ \cdot & \cdot \quad\quad\quad\quad \cdot \\ \cdot & \cdot \quad\quad\quad\quad \cdot \\ \cdot & \cdot \quad\quad\quad\quad \cdot \\ H_{1n} - S_{1n}E & H_{2n} - S_{2n}E \cdots H_{nn} - S_{nn}E \end{vmatrix} = 0$$

Such determinants have a "diagonal of symmetry" (Hermitean) and have n real roots. Further progress now depends on evaluation of H_{ij} and S_{ij}.

THE OVERLAP INTEGRAL, S_{ij}

The S_{ij} integrals are of the type

$$S_{ij} = \int X_i X_j \, d\tau$$

If i = j, then

$$S_{ij} = \int X_i X_i \, d\tau = \int X_i^2 \, d\tau = 1$$

for normalized atomic orbitals. This simplifies our original matrix to

$$\begin{vmatrix} H_{11} - E & H_{12} - S_{12}E & \cdot & \cdot & \cdot & H_{1n} - S_{1n}E \\ H_{12} - S_{12}E & H_{22} - E & \cdot & \cdot & \cdot & H_{2n} - S_{2n}E \\ \cdot & \cdot & & & & \cdot \\ \cdot & \cdot & & & & \cdot \\ H_{1n} - S_{1n}E & \cdot & \cdot & \cdot & \cdot & \cdot & \cdot & H_{nn} - E \end{vmatrix} = 0$$

When i ≠ j, if
$$S_{ij} = \int X_i X_j \, d\tau = 0$$

then X_i and X_j are said to be orthogonal. Since S_{ij} is in a sense a measure of how "non-orthogonal" X_i and X_j are, S_{ij} has been called the "non-orthogonality" integral. Orthogonal X functions are independent X functions and because X functions of orbitals widely separated in space are independent, the corresponding X's of such orbitals are expected to be orthogonal.

For s functions, it can be shown that S_{ij} varies from 0 to unity depending upon how far apart in space the orbitals are. The closer the centers of the X functions, the larger is S_{ij}. In this sense S_{ij} can be called an "overlap integral" since it is a measure of how much the orbitals i and j overlap. In the usual "zeroth" approximation of the LCAO method S_{ij} (i ≠ j) is taken equal to zero. This is by no means necessary but it does simplify the calculations considerably.

Some idea of how the magnitude of S_{ij} for the different carbon orbitals varies with the internuclear distance r_{ij} is

shown by the following graph based on calculations by
Mulliken:[2]

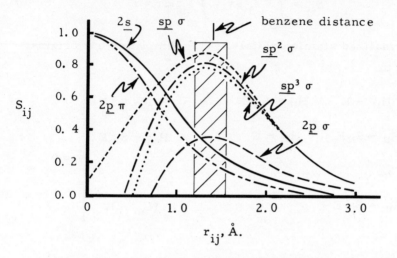

Later on we shall be concerned largely with p-π bonding, and it will be seen that the values of p-π S_{ij} range between
0.20 to 0.27 over the usual range of carbon-carbon bond distances from 1.20 to 1.54 Å. At much greater distances S_{ij}
can be safely taken as zero. The consequences of neglecting
S_{ij} are usually not very serious, at least at the level of approximation we shall be interested in here.

Exercise 2-1

The graph of S_{ij} as a function of r_{ij} shows $2p$-π
overlap to increase monotonically to unity as r_{ij} decreases. On the other hand for $2p$-σ overlap S_{ij} increases to a maximum, then goes to zero, and changes
sign at $r_{ij} < 0.7$ A. Explain.

If S_{ij} with $i \neq j$ is taken as zero, then the determinant
simplifies as shown on the next page. Further progress at
this point depends upon evaluation of the H integrals.

[2]R. S. Mulliken, Record of Chemical Progress,
Summer 1952, p. 67.

$$
\begin{vmatrix}
H_{11} - E & H_{12} & \cdots & H_{1n} \\
H_{12} & H_{22} - E & \cdots & H_{2n} \\
\cdot & \cdot & & \cdot \\
\cdot & \cdot & & \cdot \\
\cdot & \cdot & & \cdot \\
H_{1n} & H_{2n} & \cdots & H_{nn} - E
\end{vmatrix} = 0
$$

THE COULOMB INTEGRAL, α

The H integrals have the form

$$
H_{ij} = \int X_i H X_j \, d\tau
$$

If i = j, then

$$
H_{ii} = \int X_i H X_i \, d\tau
$$

To a zeroth-order approximation H_{ii} is the Coulomb energy
of an electron, with the wave function X_i in the field of atom i,
and might be regarded as but little affected by any other nuclei
farther away. This approximation, of course, will be most
valid where the surrounding atoms have no net electrical
charges. We shall take

$$
H_{ii} = \alpha_i \text{ (the \underline{Coulomb integral})}^{*}
$$

where α is a function of nuclear charge and the type of orbital.
Procedures for correcting α for the effects of neighboring
atoms will be discussed later. As here defined, α clearly is
a negative number.

---

[*]At one time q was rather widely used as a symbol for
the Coulomb integral, but this usage has generally been aban-
doned because q_i is now used to denote the charge on the i th
atom (see later).

THE RESONANCE INTEGRAL, β

We note that

$$H_{ij} = \int X_i H X_j \, d\tau \qquad \text{where } i \neq j$$

In the zeroth approximation, H_{ij} amounts to the energy of an electron in the fields of atoms i and j involving the wave functions X_i and X_j. It is usually called β_{ij}, the resonance integral.[3] β_{ij} is a function of atomic number, orbital types, and the degree of overlap. As a function of the degree of overlap β is also a function of the internuclear distance and, except for s orbitals, the angles at which the orbitals are set with respect to the internuclear line. Thus, for a given internuclear distance, the following arrangements for overlap of 2p orbitals would not have the same value of β_{ij} and S_{ij}:

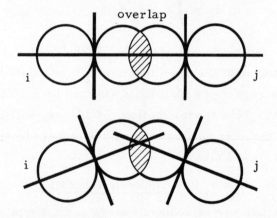

Methods for calculating β_{ij} and S_{ij} for such situations will be discussed later. In the zeroth approximation β_{ij} is neglected between all atoms that are not at the customary bond-forming distances.

[3] See Ref. 1, pp. 76-77, for reasons that justify the choice of name.

Mulliken[4] has provided data for the following graph of "semi-empirical" β against r_{ij}, for carbon $2\underline{p}$-π overlap relative to that of the isolated carbon-carbon double bond.

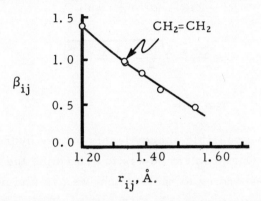

If β_{ij}, when i and j are not nearest neighbors, is set to zero, then our matrix becomes very simple since most of the H_{ij} terms vanish.

ENERGY LEVELS OF $H_2^{\oplus}$

For hydrogen molecule ion, we can now convert the original determinant

$$\begin{vmatrix} H_{11} - S_{11}E & H_{12} - S_{12}E \\ H_{12} - S_{12}E & H_{22} - S_{22}E \end{vmatrix} = 0$$

into the following determinant by the substitutions $H_{11} = \alpha_1$, $H_{22} = \alpha_2$, $H_{12} = \beta$, $S_{11} = S_{22} = 1$, and $S_{12} = 0$:

$$\begin{vmatrix} \alpha_1 - E & \beta \\ \beta & \alpha_2 - E \end{vmatrix} = 0$$

[4]R. S. Mulliken, C. Rieke, and W. G. Brown, J. Am. Chem. Soc., 63, 48 (1941).

Now, because $\alpha_1 = \alpha_2$, the nuclei being identical,

$$\alpha^2 - 2\alpha E + E^2 - \beta^2 = 0$$

or
$$E^2 - 2\alpha E + (\alpha^2 - \beta^2) = 0$$

$$E = \frac{2\alpha \pm \sqrt{4\alpha^2 - 4(\alpha^2 - \beta^2)}}{2}$$

$$= \alpha \pm \beta$$

Thus we find two possible energy levels for the hydrogen molecule ion. Our problem now is to determine the wave functions corresponding to each so that we can find out which calculated energy corresponds to the more stable state. Remembering (see p. 28) that

$$c_1(\alpha - E) + c_2\beta = 0 \qquad (1)$$
$$c_1\beta + c_2(\alpha - E) = 0 \qquad (2)$$

we have from Eq. (1) that

$$\frac{c_1}{c_2} = -\frac{\beta}{\alpha - E}$$

Now, when $E = \alpha + \beta$,

$$\frac{c_1}{c_2} = -\frac{\beta}{-\beta} = 1$$

and when $E = \alpha - \beta$,

$$\frac{c_1}{c_2} = -\frac{\beta}{\beta} = -1$$

For the energy level, $E = \alpha + \beta$, we might take

$$\psi_{\text{molecule}} = \psi = X_1 + X_2$$

However, we must be sure that ψ is normalized. This can be done as follows:

$$\int \psi^2 \, d\tau = \int (X_1 + X_2)^2 \, d\tau$$

$$= \int X_1^2 \, d\tau + \int X_2^2 \, d\tau + 2 \int X_1 X_2 \, d\tau$$

Now, if X_1 and X_2 are individually normalized and mutually orthogonal X functions, then

$$\int \psi^2 \, d\tau = 1 + 1 + 0 = 2$$

This is not a normalized ψ function. If we multipy ψ by the normalization factor $1/\sqrt{2}$, then the equation can be seen to be normalized as

$$\psi_1 \text{ (molecular orbital)} = (1/\sqrt{2})(X_1 + X_2)$$

In general, we can normalize a set of orthogonal X functions of the form $(c_1 X_1 + c_2 X_2 + \cdots c_n X_n)$ or $\left(\frac{c_1}{c_1} X_1 + \frac{c_2}{c_1} X_2 + \cdots \frac{c_n}{c_1} X_n \right)$ with a normalization factor $1/N$ where

$$N = \sqrt{c_1^2 + c_2^2 \cdots + c_n^2}$$

or

$$N = \sqrt{(c_1/c_1)^2 + (c_2/c_1)^2 + \cdots + (c_n/c_1)^2}$$

For the energy level, $E = \alpha - \beta$,

$$\psi_2 = (1/\sqrt{2})(X_1 - X_2)$$

With appropriate numerical values of α and β for $H_2^{\oplus}$, we could calculate the binding energy. Of course, the calculated value would be no better than any of our assumptions, including the basic one that a molecular orbital can be approximated by a linear combination of atomic orbitals.

Exercise 2-2

Obtain an expression for the energy of the hydrogen molecule ion on the assumption that $S_{12} = 0.25$. Find the molecular wave functions that correspond thereto.

BONDING AND ANTIBONDING ORBITALS

With respect to which wave function corresponds to the most stable state, we shall be helped by considering the electron distribution that corresponds to each. For $\psi_1 = (1/\sqrt{2})(X_1 + X_2)$ the wave functions centered on nuclei 1 and 2 have the same sign, and their cross sections can be represented graphically as follows:

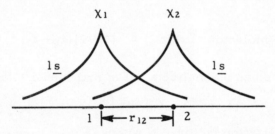

The square of the sum of $(1/\sqrt{2})(X_1 + X_2)$ is a measure of the total electron probability (not the radial probability used on p. 2) and is here represented schematically both in cross section and from above with contour lines connected between points of equal probability as shown on the next page. It will be seen that the electron will have a considerable probability between the nuclei and will act to overcome the internuclear repulsion. While we cannot be sure without more detailed calculation whether or not the overall result will be net binding, at least the orbital might be classed as a bonding orbital because of the character of its electron distribution. On this basis, β must be a negative number.

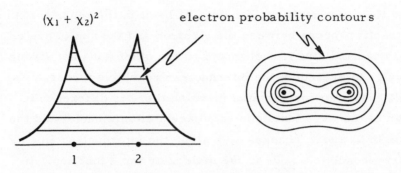

$(\chi_1 + \chi_2)^2$ electron probability contours

1   2

For the orbital $\psi_2 = (1/\sqrt{2})(\chi_1 - \chi_2)$ a similar treatment gives the following cross section and electron probability curves:

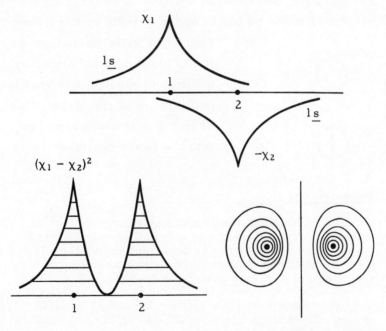

Here we see that the electron probability is zero midway between the nuclei. As a result the electron is not on the average well-positioned to pull the nuclei together, and we call this molecular orbital an antibonding molecular orbital.

Although we have only concluded that ψ_1 and ψ_2 are bonding and antibonding relative to one another, it turns out for $H_2^{\oplus}$ [5] that the lower electronic state is in fact bonding and the upper state antibonding, at least in the sense that the attractive forces between the electron and the nuclei are on the one hand strong enough and on the other hand not strong enough to overcome the internuclear repulsive forces. We will encounter many states in which there is difference in sign of the wave functions on adjacent atomic nuclei and the sum of X_i and X_j changes sign along the internuclear line as corresponds to a node in the molecular wave function. In general this does not mean that the nuclei cannot be bonded together; however, wave functions with nodes are expected to contribute less bonding than those without nodes.

For the $H_2^{\oplus}$ molecule ion we have two energy levels in which electrons might be put in order to build up the compound in a manner analogous to the building up of atoms by addition of electrons to atomic orbitals. For the stable state of $H_2^{\oplus}$ the electron would go into the lower orbital.

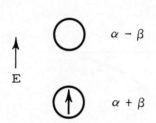

E

$\alpha - \beta$

$\alpha + \beta$

Exercise 2-3

a. Calculate the resonance energy of $H_2^{\oplus}$ in units of β with reference to a hypothetical standard state where the electron is localized on nucleus 1, i.e. the electron is described by the wave function X_1. Neglect overlap; take $S_{ij} = 0$ when $i \neq j$.

b. Show that $(1/\sqrt{2})(X_1 - X_2)$ and $(1/\sqrt{2})(X_2 - X_1)$ are equally acceptable ψ functions for the antibonding state of $H_2^{\oplus}$.

[5] See the curves given in p. 79 of Ref. 1 for the energy of $H_2^{\oplus}$ as a function of internuclear distance.

Exercise 2-4

Calculate the resonance energy of $H_2^{\oplus}$ as in Exercise 2-3 taking $S_{12} = 0.25$.

THE HYDROGEN MOLECULE

We might well be tempted to take the molecular orbitals obtained for $H_2^{\oplus}$ and put in two paired electrons in the lowest level to calculate the energy of H_2. This procedure would predict that if $\alpha + \beta$ is the electronic binding energy for $H_2^{\oplus}$, then $2\alpha + 2\beta$ would be the binding energy for H_2. In fact, the cal-

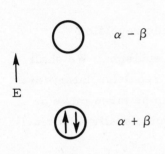

culated values of $\alpha + \beta$ for both systems (29.7 e.v. for $H_2^{\oplus}$ and 26.5 e.v. for H_2) are amazingly close, if we define the binding energies as the energy of putting the electron(s) into the framework of the nuclei at the equilibrium distance. Nonetheless, the agreement must be regarded as the result of coincidence for the following reasons: First, the internuclear distances in $H_2^{\oplus}$ and H_2 are very different, 1.06 Å and 0.74 Å respectively, so that there is not the slightest justification for assuming α and β (or S_{12}) to be the same for $H_2^{\oplus}$ and H_2. Second, the coulombic repulsion between the two electrons in H_2 is calculated to be 17.8 e.v., and no account was taken of such repulsion in assuming the binding energy of H_2 is twice $\alpha + \beta$ for $H_2^{\oplus}$.

Exercise 2-5

Calculate $\alpha + \beta$ for $H_2^{\oplus}$ and H_2 from the following data: The Coulomb internuclear repulsions of $H_2^{\oplus}$ and H_2 are +13.5 and +19.3 e.v. respectively; the ionization potential of hydrogen is -13.6 e.v.; the bond energy of H_2 is 4.72 e.v.; and the energy of the reaction $H \cdot + H^{\oplus} \longrightarrow H_2^{\oplus}$ is 2.64 e.v.

Clearly, we must be cautious in assuming that α and β are the same for compounds with different numbers of electrons but similar molecular orbitals. Now, if we take that for H_2 the electron binding energy E is equal to $2\alpha + 2\beta$, where α and β are proper values for H_2, then α and β are not so clearly defined as before because we now have taken into account interelectronic repulsion between the two electrons without explicitly putting in interelectronic repulsion terms. Thus, we might write

$$E = 2\alpha + 2\beta$$

or

$$E = 2\alpha' + 2\beta' + \text{ interelectronic repulsion}$$

where α and β include interelectronic repulsion. We shall have more to say about interelectronic repulsion later; for the present we shall consider that it can be taken more or less into account by selecting proper (and usually empirical) values for α and β.

LOCALIZED BONDS

The molecular orbital treatment of $H_2^{\oplus}$ can be applied to organic molecules such as CH_4 or $CH_2{=}CH_2$ in two different ways: First, molecular orbitals can be set up as linear combinations of all of the atomic orbitals of the molecule, their energies can be calculated, and the appropriate number of electrons can be put in. This is necessarily a complicated procedure and not of great interest to organic chemists because "absolute" numbers for CH_4 and $CH_2{=}CH_2$ are less useful than comparisons relative to other molecules of the same general type. The second and simpler approach is to make the approximation that electrons in some, or most, of the bonds are "localized". Localized electrons are assumed not to contribute importantly to the electronic character of the bonds in the rest of the molecule.

Thus, for ethylene, we might consider each of the bonds to be localized and the electrons in each to act independently of the electrons in the other bonds. We are then taking each bond as a sort of localized "molecular orbital" of the type involved in $H_2^{\oplus}$ but are considering different kinds of atomic orbitals. Generally speaking this approximation is quite useful. The

localized π bond

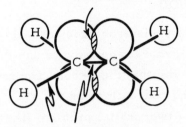

localized σ bond

reason is that for most reactions of simple saturated and unsaturated systems, the bonds are usually made and broken in substantial independence of one another. Major difficulties come when one attempts to predict and interpret the behavior of conjugated unsaturated compounds.

Butadiene is known to be a substance in which the double bonds can react simultaneously as, for example, in the Diels-Alder reaction and in 1,4 additions of halogens. In the simple molecular orbital treatment, butadiene is treated as a system with localized σ bonds and delocalized π bonds.

delocalized π bonds

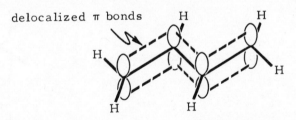

The results can be compared with those calculated for the localized model.

localized π bond

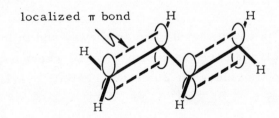

whose properties might be deduced from those of ethylene
and/or the expectations based on the usual bond energies.

ETHYLENE BY THE LCAO METHOD

Ethylene is easily treated as a π-electron problem and
provides a good starting point for a general approach to unsaturated molecules. We shall assume that the σ-bond framework has conventional properties and concentrate on the π
electrons. Ethylene then becomes a two-orbital problem like
H_2. The 2p orbitals of carbon are here represented with +
and − lobes because the X function of a 2p orbital has a node
in (and changes sign below) the plane, which is perpendicular
to the axis of the orbital and passes through the nucleus.

$$\psi_{\pi\text{ electrons}} = c_1 X_1 + c_2 X_2$$

If we proceed as with hydrogen, the mathematical operations
are the same so that we have

$$E_1 = \alpha + \beta \quad \psi_1 = (1/\sqrt{2})(X_1 + X_2)$$

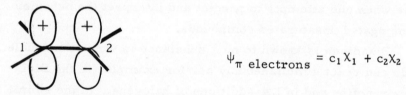

$$E_2 = \alpha - \beta \quad \psi_2 = (1/\sqrt{2})(X_1 - X_2)$$

node

The energy levels are as shown, and in the lowest state
two electrons have the energy $2(\alpha + \beta)$ where α and β have
appropriate values for 2p carbon orbitals overlapping in the
π manner.

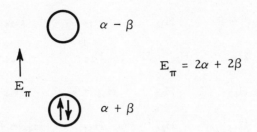

$$E_\pi = 2\alpha + 2\beta$$

Exercise 2-7

Consider how the energy E_π of acetylene might be calculated and possible difficulties in comparison of the value so obtained with E_π calculated for ethylene.

BUTADIENE, E_π

For butadiene we can make a calculation of the π-electron energy by considering that the σ-bond framework is such as to have π overlap of four parallel $2\underline{p}$ orbitals.

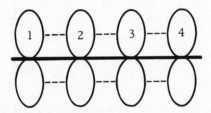

Our starting wave function will then be

$$\psi = c_1 X_1 + c_2 X_2 + c_3 X_3 + c_4 X_4$$

where the normalization condition must hold. The possible values of E that correspond to this equation are the roots of a determinant where S_{ij} ($i \neq j$) has been set to zero as shown by the determinant on the next page. Remembering that $H_{ii} = \alpha_i$, we shall assume that $\alpha_1 = \alpha_2 = \alpha_3 = \alpha_4 = \alpha$, since the surroundings of each carbon are similar although not identical. This assumption is not necessary if we have any better basis for evaluating the individual α's. Of course, in any case, we would expect $\alpha_1 = \alpha_4$ and $\alpha_2 = \alpha_3$.

$$
\begin{vmatrix}
H_{11} - E & H_{12} & H_{13} & H_{14} \\
H_{12} & H_{22} - E & H_{23} & H_{24} \\
H_{13} & H_{23} & H_{33} - E & H_{34} \\
H_{14} & H_{24} & H_{34} & H_{44} - E
\end{vmatrix} = 0
$$

For the off-diagonal terms, $H_{ij} = \beta_{ij}$, we shall here assume that $\beta_{12} = \beta_{23} = \beta_{34} = \beta$ (for adjacent atoms) and that $\beta_{13} = \beta_{14} = \beta_{24} = 0$ (nonadjacent atoms). The values of β_{12} and β_{23} will not be exactly equal but can be corrected as desired by the graph on p. 33 . We can now rewrite the determinant as

$$
\begin{vmatrix}
\alpha - E & \beta & 0 & 0 \\
\beta & \alpha - E & \beta & 0 \\
0 & \beta & \alpha - E & \beta \\
0 & 0 & \beta & \alpha - E
\end{vmatrix} = 0
$$

To simplify the notation we divide through the determinant by β:

$$
\begin{vmatrix}
(\alpha - E)/\beta & 1 & 0 & 0 \\
1 & (\alpha - E)/\beta & 1 & 0 \\
0 & 1 & (\alpha - E)/\beta & 1 \\
0 & 0 & 1 & (\alpha - E)/\beta
\end{vmatrix} = 0
$$

Now, letting $(\alpha - E)/\beta = x$, we can write

$$\begin{vmatrix} x & 1 & 0 & 0 \\ 1 & x & 1 & 0 \\ 0 & 1 & x & 1 \\ 0 & 0 & 1 & x \end{vmatrix} = 0$$

As one way of breaking down the butadiene secular determinant (or a general secular determinant of n rows and n
columns), we can take the top row of n terms and multiply
each of the terms by the corresponding (n th) cofactor with
a + sign for the product if n is odd and a − sign if n is even.
The cofactor used here is the determinant with the top row
and n th column removed:

$$x \begin{vmatrix} x & 1 & 0 \\ 1 & x & 1 \\ 0 & 1 & x \end{vmatrix} - 1 \cdot \begin{vmatrix} 1 & 1 & 0 \\ 0 & x & 1 \\ 0 & 1 & x \end{vmatrix} + 0 \cdot \begin{vmatrix} 1 & x & 0 \\ 0 & 1 & 1 \\ 0 & 0 & x \end{vmatrix} - 0 \cdot \begin{vmatrix} 1 & x & 1 \\ 0 & 1 & x \\ 0 & 0 & 1 \end{vmatrix} = 0$$

Breaking down the third-order determinants and discarding
all zero terms gives

$$x^2 \begin{vmatrix} x & 1 \\ 1 & x \end{vmatrix} - x \begin{vmatrix} 1 & 1 \\ 0 & x \end{vmatrix} - \begin{vmatrix} x & 1 \\ 1 & x \end{vmatrix} + \begin{vmatrix} 0 & 1 \\ 0 & x \end{vmatrix} = 0$$

Cross-multiplication of the two-row determinants leads to
the following equations:

$$x^2(x^2 - 1) - x(x) - (x^2 - 1) + 0 = 0$$

and

$$x^4 - x^2 - x^2 - x^2 + 1 = 0$$

$$x^4 - 3x^2 + 1 = 0$$

$$x = \pm \sqrt{\frac{3 \pm \sqrt{9 - 4}}{2}} = \pm 1.61804, \pm 0.61804$$

Therefore, since $x = (\alpha - E)/\beta$, we have the following energy levels and occupied orbitals for four π electrons:

The precision to which x has been calculated here is not meant to reflect the accuracy of the MO method but will be seen later to be helpful in aiding cross checks on the arithmetical operations.

Exercise 2-8

Calculate by the LCAO MO method whether the linear $(H-H-H^\oplus)$ state or the triangular state

of $H_3^\oplus$ is the more stable. Do the same for H_3 and $H_3^\ominus$. (Answers may be checked against the sample calculations given in Appendix I.)

BUTADIENE RESONANCE ENERGY

To calculate the resonance energy of butadiene, we first compute the value of E_π that the molecule would have if the four π electrons were localized into 1, 2- and 3, 4- double bonds. Such localization has the effect of making $\beta_{23} = 0$. The determinant is then

$$\begin{vmatrix} x & 1 & 0 & 0 \\ 1 & x & 0 & 0 \\ 0 & 0 & x & 1 \\ 0 & 0 & 1 & x \end{vmatrix} = 0$$

which has the roots $x = \pm 1, \quad \pm 1$; $\quad E = \alpha \pm \beta, \quad \alpha \pm \beta$.

Exercise 2-9

Verify that the roots of the determinant for local-ized butadiene are $x = \pm 1, \quad \pm 1$.

The two lowest π-electron orbitals of localized butadiene are seen to have the energy $\alpha + \beta$ while the two highest orbitals have the energy $\alpha - \beta$. These are, of course, just the orbital energies expected for two isolated ethylene molecules. We expect the four π electrons to go into the lowest orbitals as follows:

The delocalization or resonance energy DE_π of delocalized butadiene equals $(4\alpha + 4.4720\beta) - (4\alpha + 4\beta) = 0.472\beta$. The resonance energy calculated in this way comes out in units

of one parameter β, the α terms being the same for the delocalized and localized models. Since the resonance energy
calculated for benzene by the procedure used for butadiene
is 2β and the experimental value for benzene is 36 kcal./
mole, [*] β is usually taken for carbon systems as 18 kcal./
mole. If S_{ij} is not set equal to zero for $i \neq j$, then a
different value of β must be used. With $\beta = 18$ kcal./mole,
DE_π for butadiene is 8.5 kcal./mole, which number is to be
compared to a 3 kcal./mole "experimental" value. The sig-
nificance of the degree of agreement between these numbers
turns out to be a rather personal value judgment. Some quar-
ters appear to regard the agreement as an unmitigated triumph
considering the approximations involved; others take the discrepancy as being so large as to indicate the treatment to be
of no value whatsoever. The position taken here will be intermediate between these extremes.

Exercise 2-10

Calculate the resonance energy in units of β for
butadiene using numerical values of β such as are appropriate for the bond distances involved (see p. 33).
Use the reported 1.37 Å for the 1,2- and 3,4-bonds and
1.47 Å for the 2,3-bond in the delocalized molecule.
Use 1.34 Å for the 1,2- and 3,4-bonds in the localized
form.

THE BUTADIENE WAVE FUNCTIONS

The delocalized butadiene ψ functions are of the form
$c_1X_1 + c_2X_2 + c_3X_3 + c_4X_4$, with the magnitude and sign of c_n

[*]This is the most widely quoted benzene resonance
energy, but one must recognize that resonance energy is an
unusually artificial concept in that it represents the difference in energy of formation expected for some purely hypothetical molecule and an actual molecule. The choice of
hypothetical model is arbitrary to the point of exasperation.
Estimates of the "true" resonance energy of benzene range
from 10 to 70 kcal./mole.

depending upon the energy level. To calculate c_n values we can proceed as follows: We obtain the ratios c_n/c_1 by the equation

$$\frac{c_n}{c_1} = + \frac{(\text{cofactor})_n}{(\text{cofactor})_1} \qquad \text{if } n = \text{odd}$$

$$\frac{c_n}{c_1} = - \frac{(\text{cofactor})_n}{(\text{cofactor})_1} \qquad \text{if } n = \text{even}$$

The ratios have to be normalized to get the final coefficients (cf. p. 35).

We shall calculate the coefficients of the occupied orbitals with $x = -1.61804$ and -0.61804.

$$\frac{c_1}{c_1} = \frac{+\begin{vmatrix} x & 1 & 0 \\ 1 & x & 1 \\ 0 & 1 & x \end{vmatrix}}{+\begin{vmatrix} x & 1 & 0 \\ 1 & x & 1 \\ 0 & 1 & x \end{vmatrix}} = 1$$

$$\frac{c_2}{c_1} = \frac{-\begin{vmatrix} 1 & 1 & 0 \\ 0 & x & 1 \\ 0 & 1 & x \end{vmatrix}}{+\begin{vmatrix} x & 1 & 0 \\ 1 & x & 1 \\ 0 & 1 & x \end{vmatrix}} = \frac{-(x^2 - 1)}{x^3 - 2x}$$

$$\frac{c_3}{c_1} = \frac{+\begin{vmatrix} 1 & x & 0 \\ 0 & 1 & 1 \\ 0 & 0 & x \end{vmatrix}}{+\begin{vmatrix} x & 1 & 0 \\ 1 & x & 1 \\ 0 & 1 & x \end{vmatrix}} = \frac{x}{x^3 - 2x} = \frac{1}{x^2 - 2}$$

$$\frac{c_4}{c_1} = \frac{-\begin{vmatrix} 1 & x & 1 \\ 0 & 1 & x \\ 0 & 0 & 1 \end{vmatrix}}{+\begin{vmatrix} x & 1 & 0 \\ 1 & x & 1 \\ 0 & 1 & x \end{vmatrix}} = \frac{-1}{x^3 - 2x}$$

It will be convenient to tabulate the results as shown in Table 2-1. Here c_n is obtained as the quotient of c_n/c_1 divided by $\sqrt{\Sigma(c_n/c_1)^2}$.

Table 2-1

Calculation of MO Coefficients for Butadiene

$$x = -1.61804$$

n	$\dfrac{c_n}{c_1}$	$\left(\dfrac{c_n}{c_1}\right)^2$	c_n
1	1.0000	1.0000	0.3717
2	1.6180	2.61799	0.6015
3	1.6180	2.61799	0.6015
4	1.0000	1.0000	0.3717

$$\Sigma (c_n/c_1)^2 = 7.23598 = 2.6900^2$$

(Table 2-1 continued)

$$x = -0.61804$$

n	$\dfrac{c_n}{c_1}$	$\left(\dfrac{c_n}{c_1}\right)^2$	c_n
1	1.0000	1.0000	0.6015
2	0.6180	0.38197	0.3717
3	-0.6180	0.38197	-0.3717
4	-1.0000	1.0000	-0.6015

$$\Sigma\,(c_n/c_1)^2 = 2.7639 = 1.6625^2$$

The final wave functions are:

$$\psi_1 = 0.3717X_1 + 0.6015X_2 + 0.6015X_3 + 0.3717X_4$$

$$\psi_2 = 0.6015X_1 + 0.3717X_2 - 0.3717X_3 - 0.6015X_4$$

$$\psi_3 = 0.6015X_1 - 0.3717X_2 - 0.3717X_3 + 0.6015X_4$$

$$\psi_4 = 0.3717X_1 - 0.6015X_2 + 0.6015X_3 - 0.3717X_4$$

We can sketch out schematically the butadiene ψ functions as follows:

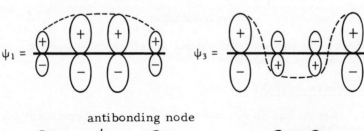

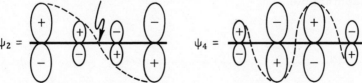

Wherever the wave function changes sign between the nuclei
a node results. Note that the calculated energy of the orbitals
increases with the number of nodes. The highest orbital is
antibonding between each pair of nuclei. In contrast, the
lowest orbital has no nodes and is "completely" bonding.

Exercise 2-11

Verify that ψ_2 has the energy $\alpha + 0.61804\beta$ by use
of the equation, $E = \int \psi_2 H \psi_2 \, d\tau / \int \psi_2{}^2 \, d\tau$.

Exercise 2-12

Verify the coefficients given for ψ_3 and ψ_4.

Exercise 2-13

Calculate the coefficients for butadiene with localized π bonds.

Exercise 2-14

Calculate the π-energy levels, DE_π, and the final
wave functions for bicyclobutadiene. (The answers may
be checked against the sample calculations in Appendix
I.)

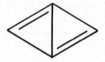

bicyclobutadiene

Sketch out the wave functions schematically showing
the various nodal lines.

Exercise 2-15

Set up but do not solve the secular determinant for
naphthalene.

Chapter 3

Bond Orders, Free Valence Indexes, and Charge Distributions

THE MOBILE BOND ORDER, p_{ij}

The relative π binding between pairs of adjacent nuclei is expected to be related to the coefficients of the atomic orbitals on the atoms between which the bond is formed. For butadiene we can qualitatively assess the binding between adjacent nuclei by inspection of the occupied orbitals as follows:

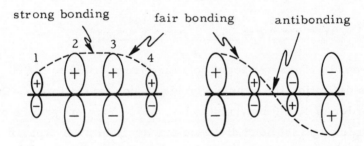

This approach has been put on a quantitative basis by Coulson through p_{ij}, the "mobile bond order" between adjacent atoms i and j. This is defined by the equation

$$p_{ij} = \sum^{\psi_{occ.}} Nc_i c_j$$

where N = number of electrons in a given occupied orbital; c_i, c_j = the normalized coefficients for atoms i and j for the

53

occupied orbital; and the sum is taken over all of the occupied orbitals. Clearly $c_i \cdot c_j$ will be positive when a given molecular orbital is bonding between two given nuclei and negative when it is antibonding. For the 1,2–bond of butadiene,

$$p_{12} = (N_1 c_1 c_2)_{\psi_1} + (N_2 c_1 c_2)_{\psi_2}$$
$$= 2 \times 0.3717 \times 0.6015 + 2 \times 0.6015 \times 0.3717$$
$$= 0.8942$$

and for the 2,3–bond,

$$p_{23} = 2 \times 0.6015 \times 0.6015 - 2 \times 0.3717 \times 0.3717$$
$$= 0.4473$$

The π–mobile bond orders for butadiene are:

$$\begin{array}{ccccccc} & 0.8942 & & 0.4473 & & 0.8942 & \\ CH_2 &\text{----}& CH &\cdots& CH &\text{----}& CH_2 \end{array}$$

If we take the σ bonds as 1.0 bonds, then we can write for the total C–C bond orders:

$$\begin{array}{ccccccc} & 1.8942 & & 1.4473 & & 1.8942 & \\ CH_2 &\text{----}& CH &\cdots& CH &\text{----}& CH_2 \end{array}$$

The π–bond orders are found to range from 0.000 to 1.000. By this definition the benzene bonds do not have a total C–C bond order of 1.500 but, instead, 1.667. Various graphs of bond order against bond distance are available. A typical relationship is shown in Figure 3–1. The bond lengths predicted for butadiene by the simple MO treatment are $r_{12} = 1.36$ Å and $r_{23} = 1.45$ Å. The reported values are quite close: $r_{12} = 1.37$ Å and $r_{23} = 1.47$ Å. Rather good agreement has been reported between calculated and experimental bond lengths in polynuclear aromatic hydrocarbons. Typical results are shown on the next page for naphthalene and anthracene[1] (with distances in Å and calculated values in parentheses). Despite

[1] D. W. J. Cruickshank and A. P. Robertson, Acta Cryst., 6, 698 (1953).

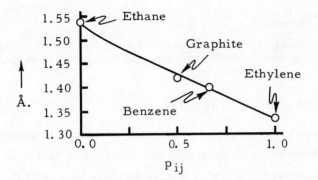

Fig. 3-1. Typical bond order - bond distance relationship for C—C bonds.

the respectable agreement between calculated and experimental
π-bond distances, the approach here, which involves assuming
that the length of the 2, 3 bond in localized butadiene would be
1. 54 Å, has been severely and probably justly criticized.[2]

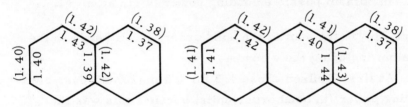

The Coulson π-bond orders provide a useful check on
the calculation of E_π through the relation

$$E_\pi = 2\beta(\Sigma p_{ij}) + N\alpha$$

Thus, for butadiene,

$$E_\pi = 2\beta(2p_{12} + p_{23}) + 4\alpha$$
$$= 2\beta(2 \times 0.8942 + 0.4473) + 4\alpha$$
$$= 4\alpha + 4.471\beta$$

[2]M. J. S. Dewar and H. N. Schmeising, Tetrahedron
11, 96 (1960); these authors offer a corrected graph of bond
distance vs. π-bond order (calculated including overlap) that
gives 1.47 Å for $p_{ij} = 0$.

Exercise 3-1

Calculate the mobile bond orders for bicyclobutadiene. (A check on the answers is available in Appendix I.)

THE FREE VALENCE INDEX, $\mathscr{F}_i$

One possible approach to the study of chemical reactivity is to determine the degree that the atoms in a molecule are bonded to adjacent atoms relative to their theoretical maximum bonding power. If particular atoms are not much bonded compared to the maximum, we could say that they have considerable "free valence" and especially reactive positions. Coulson defines a free valence index, $\mathscr{F}_i$, for atom i as follows:

$$\mathscr{F}_i = \text{maximum possible bonding power of } i\text{th atom} - \Sigma p_{ij}$$

where Σp_{ij} is the sum of the bond orders of all bonds to the ith atom including the σ bonds.

At first Coulson chose 4.5 for the maximum possible bonding power (in bond order units) because this was the highest degree of bonding he encountered in the usual calculations; however, the theoretical maximum is easily shown to be 4.732. Consider the molecule trimethylenemethane:

trimethylenemethane

The central atom of trimethylenemethane is bonded by three σ bonds and three π bonds to its neighbors. Since the CH_2

groups are not π bonded to any other atoms, they can devote full attention to the central atom. A simple calculation shows that Σp_{ij} for the central carbon in $C(CH_2)_3 = 4.732$.

Exercise 3-2

Calculate the energy levels, DE_π, and bond orders for symmetrical trimethylenemethane. Verify that Σp_{ij} for the central atom is 4.732. Calculate an energy of conversion of trimethylenemethane into methylene-cyclopropane.

For butadiene

$$\mathcal{F}_1 = \mathcal{F}_4 = 4.732 - (2p_{C-H} + p_{12,\,\sigma} + p_{12,\,\pi})$$

$$= 4.732 - (2 + 1 + 0.8942) = 0.8378$$

$$\mathcal{F}_2 = \mathcal{F}_3 = 4.732 - (3 + 0.4473 + 0.8942) = 0.3905$$

From the $\mathcal{F}$ values we can argue that butadiene could well be more reactive to neutral nonpolar reagents, such as free radicals at the 1 and 4 carbons, than at the 2 and 3 carbons. Neutral nonpolar reagents are specified here so as to avoid commitments that might have to be modified later by consideration of charge distribution effects.

The usual way of reporting the results of MO calculations of free valence indexes, bond orders, and DE_π follows:

$$DE_\pi = 0.472\beta$$

Exercise 3-3

Calculate $\mathcal{F}_i$ for bicyclobutadiene. (For a check on the answers see Appendix I.)

Typical calculated $\mathcal{X}_i$ values for a number of substances are shown below; a reasonably obvious correlation exists with free radical reactivity:

0.000

$\uparrow$

$C(CH_2)_3$

0.73

$\nearrow$

$CH_2{=}CH_2$

1.04

$\nearrow$

$-CH_2\cdot$

0.23

$\nearrow$

0.92

$\nearrow$

$CH_2{=}\!\!\!\!=\!\!\!\!=CH_2$

1.73

$\nearrow$

$CH_3\cdot$

Note that di-p-xylylene is just on the borderline of being so self-reactive as to prohibit isolation as a chemical individual.

CHARGE DISTRIBUTIONS, q_i

We can calculate deviations from the normal electron density at a given π-bonded atom by summing the electron probabilities corresponding to the contributions of the particular atomic orbital to the various occupied orbitals. Appropriate corrections may have to be made for formal charges resulting from the σ bonds to obtain the overall charge. Normal quadrivalent carbon is neutral. If a carbon forms three σ bonds and is also π bonded, it will be neutral if there is an average of one electron in its $2p\pi$-bonded orbital. Thus, if q_i is taken as the deviation from neutrality of such a carbon, we may define q_i by

$$q_i = 1.000 - \sum^{\psi_{occ.}} Nc_i^2$$

where N is the number of electrons in a particular occupied molecular orbital ψ_n and c_i is the coefficient of the atomic orbital X_i in ψ_n.

For butadiene,

$$q_1 = q_4 = 1.000 - (Nc_1{}^2)_{\psi_1} - (Nc_1{}^2)_{\psi_2}$$

$$= 1.000 - 2(0.3717)^2 - 2(0.6015)^2 = 0.000$$

$$q_2 = q_3 = 1.000 - 2(0.6015)^2 - 2(0.3717)^2 = 0.000$$

Thus, the average charges at each of the carbons of butadiene are equal and zero. Summing up the charges to get the total net charge provides a useful check on the calculated values of the coefficients.

Our complete molecular diagram for butadiene is now

$$DE_\pi = 0.472\beta$$

Here the numbers below the carbons represent the calculated deviations from the normal electron distribution.

Exercise 3-4

   Calculate q_i for bicyclobutadiene. (The answers may be checked against Appendix I.)

SELF-CONSISTENT FIELDS

   Butadiene is calculated by the simple MO method to have the same average number of π electrons at each atom. Therefore, it is often designated as a molecule with a self-consistent field. The self-consistent field calculated for butadiene is important in lending credence to the validity of of the assumption that $\beta_{12} = \beta_{23}$ and particularly that $\alpha_1 = \alpha_2$.

It has been shown by Coulson and Rushbrooke[3] that alternant
π–bonded hydrocarbons or hydrocarbon radicals (AH) will
always have self–consistent fields. "Alternant" is defined
as applying to those systems that can be "starred" on alternant atoms with no stars adjacent to one another. Cyclic
alternant hydrocarbons can only contain even–membered
rings. Examples of some alternant (AH) and nonalternant
(NAH) systems follow:

Alternant,
"starrable"

Non–alternant,
"non–starrable"

Exercise 3–5

Calculate DE_π, p_{ij}, $\mathscr{F}_i$, and q_i for the allyl radical,
carbonium ion, and carbanion. Sketch out the molecular
orbitals for the allyl system.

For nonalternant hydrocarbons we might expect the simple
LCAO method to become somewhat less reliable because the
presence of a nonself–consistent field really requires that the
Coulomb integral of each atom be corrected for the charges on
neighboring atoms. Procedures for this purpose are available.[4]

[3]C. A. Coulson and G. S. Rushbrooke, Proc. Camb. Phil.
Soc., 36, 193 (1940).

[4]G. W. Wheland and D. E. Mann, J. Chem. Phys., 17,
264 (1949).

Chapter 4

Application of Group Theory
to Simplification of MO
Determinants

THE PRINCIPAL practical difficulty in molecular orbital calculations of molecules with any degree of complexity is the breaking down of the secular determinant. We have seen how the process is carried out with the four-row determinant for butadiene. The breaking down of a corresponding ten-row determinant for naphthalene (Exercise 2–15) is a rather time-consuming operation. If a large, high-speed digital computer is available, practically any interesting π-bonded molecule can be handled by the simple LCAO method. Programs are available for solution of the determinants, calculation of the bond orders, $\mathfrak{F}_i$ values, and charge distributions.

In the present chapter we shall consider how group theory may be used in a practical way to simplify MO calculations. However, if the reader has access to a high-speed digital computer and has no urge to be able to make MO calculations while swinging in a hammock beside a mountain lake, not much is to be gained by further study of the balance of this chapter.

THE BUTADIENE DETERMINANT

The wave function $\psi = c_1 X_1 + c_2 X_2 + c_3 X_3 + c_4 X_4$ for butadiene has been shown to give the determinant

$$\begin{vmatrix} \alpha - E & \beta & 0 & 0 \\ \beta & \alpha - E & \beta & 0 \\ 0 & \beta & \alpha - E & \beta \\ 0 & 0 & \beta & \alpha - E \end{vmatrix} = 0$$

If we were to take advantage of the symmetry of butadiene and write

$$\psi = \frac{c_1}{\sqrt{2}} (X_1 \pm X_4) + \frac{c_2}{\sqrt{2}} (X_2 \pm X_3)$$

the determinant would be very substantially simplified. If we choose the plus signs of the last equation, we have

$$\psi = \frac{c_1}{\sqrt{2}} (X_1 + X_4) + \frac{c_2}{\sqrt{2}} (X_2 + X_3)$$

which, in the variation treatment, gives the following two-row determinant:

$$\begin{vmatrix} \frac{1}{2} \int (X_1 + X_4) H (X_1 + X_4)\, d\tau - E & \frac{1}{2} \int (X_1 + X_4) H (X_2 + X_3)\, d\tau \\ \frac{1}{2} \int (X_1 + X_4) H (X_2 + X_3)\, d\tau & \frac{1}{2} \int (X_2 + X_3) H (X_2 + X_3)\, d\tau - E \end{vmatrix} = 0$$

$$\begin{vmatrix} \frac{1}{2} (H_{11} + H_{44} + 2H_{14}) - E & \frac{1}{2} (H_{12} + H_{13} + H_{24} + H_{34}) \\ \frac{1}{2} (H_{12} + H_{13} + H_{24} + H_{34}) & \frac{1}{2} (H_{22} + H_{33} + 2H_{23}) - E \end{vmatrix} = 0$$

$$\begin{vmatrix} \alpha - E & \beta \\ \beta & \alpha + \beta - E \end{vmatrix} = \begin{vmatrix} x & 1 \\ 1 & x + 1 \end{vmatrix} = 0$$

$$x^2 + x - 1 = 0$$

$$x = \frac{-1 \pm \sqrt{5}}{2} = -1.6180, \ +0.6180$$

Use of the minus signs in the same way gives

$$\begin{vmatrix} x & 1 \\ 1 & x - 1 \end{vmatrix} = 0$$

$$x = +1.6180, \ -0.6180$$

This approach gives two much simpler determinants than the one found before and greatly reduces the labor of computation of the molecular orbital coefficients c_i. The trick is to use the right combinations of coefficients and to group together the orbitals that are equivalent because of molecular symmetry. This process is expedited by use of elementary group theory.

Exercise 4-1

Investigate the consequences of using $\psi = (c_1/\sqrt{2})(X_1 + X_4) + (c_2/\sqrt{2})(X_2 - X_3)$ and $\psi = (c_1/\sqrt{2})(X_1 - X_4) + (c_2/\sqrt{2})(X_2 + X_3)$ in the variational treatment of butadiene.

SYMMETRY OPERATIONS

The emphasis here will be on practical computations, and no effort will be made to bring out the underlying theory. We shall use only two-fold symmetry axes. For three-fold and higher symmetry axes making the proper choice of degenerate functions is often as much or more labor than solving the unsimplified determinants. No error will be made by assuming that a molecule has <u>less</u> symmetry than it actually has.

Consider naphthalene. It has ten π-electron centers and three two-fold symmetry axes passing through the center of the molecule at 90° to one another:

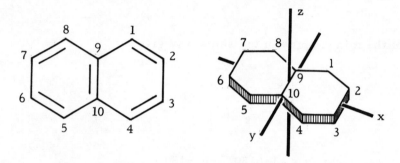

Turning the formula 180° around the z axis (the c_2^z operation) changes the position of the numbers of the atomic orbital functions centered on each atom:

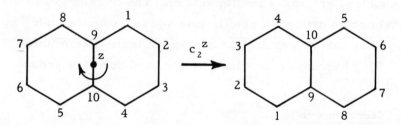

The changes ($1 \rightarrow 5$, $2 \rightarrow 6$, etc.) are usefully tabulated as follows (where E, the "identity operation", does not change the numbers):

E	c_2^z
1	5
2	6
3	7

E	c_2^z
4	8
5	1
6	2
7	3
8	4
9	10
10	9

The operations c_2^y and c_2^x proceed in the same way

so that the complete table of numbering changes is

E	c_2^z	c_2^y	c_2^x
1	5	8	4
2	6	7	3
3	7	6	2
4	8	5	1
5	1	4	8
6	2	3	7
7	3	2	6
8	4	1	5
9	10	9	10
10	9	10	9
10	0	2	0

The numbers at the bottom of the table below the dotted line represent how many atomic positions remain <u>unchanged</u> by the operation at the head of the column. We shall show in the next section how these numbers can be used in conjunction with the D_{2v} character table to obtain the size (in rows) of the various determinants that will be involved.

Exercise 4-2

Carry out the D_{2v} operations on benzene.

CHARACTER TABLES, D_{2v}

The D_{2v} character table has vertical columns corresponding to the D_{2v} symmetry operations E, c_2^z, c_2^y, and c_2^x. The horizontal rows Γ_1, Γ_2, Γ_3, and Γ_4 lead to the various possible proper combinations of arithmetical signs of the χ functions:

	E	c_2^z	c_2^y	c_2^x
Γ_1	1	1	1	1
Γ_2	1	1	-1	-1
Γ_3	1	-1	1	-1
Γ_4	1	-1	-1	1

Each Γ leads to a determinant of n rows where n is the "dot product" (sum of the products of the respective terms in Γ and their counterparts below the dotted line in the table of results of the symmetry operations) divided by the number of symmetry operations (here four). To illustrate:

For Γ_1, n = (1 x 10 + 1 x 0 + 1 x 2 + 1 x 0) $\div$ 4 = 3
For Γ_2, n = (1 x 10 + 1 x 0 - 1 x 2 - 1 x 0) $\div$ 4 = 2
For Γ_3, n = (1 x 10 - 1 x 0 + 1 x 2 - 1 x 0) $\div$ 4 = 3
For Γ_4, n = (1 x 10 - 1 x 0 - 1 x 2 + 1 x 0) $\div$ 4 = 2

Thus, for naphthalene, we find that the MO computational problem is reduced by group theory from a ten-row determinant to two three-row determinants (Γ_1 and Γ_3) and two two-row determinants (Γ_2 and Γ_4).

Exercise 4-3

a. Determine what degree determinants benzene will give in the simple LCAO method when treated as having D_{2v} symmetry.

b. Cyclobutadiene can be treated as a D_{2v} system in two ways:

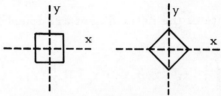

Find the order of the determinant that corresponds to each choice of axes. From these results and those obtained with naphthalene and benzene in part (a) of this problem, evolve a general rule for the maximum and minimum size of the determinant depending upon the number of orbitals and whether they fall on or off the symmetry axes.

THE TRIAL WAVE FUNCTION

The proper combinations of X functions for naphthalene are obtained for the separate Γ's as the dot product of each horizontal row of the character table with the table of transpositions under the symmetry operations. Thus, for Γ_1, we have

$$X_1 + X_5 + X_8 + X_4$$
$$X_2 + X_6 + X_7 + X_3$$
$$X_3 + X_7 + X_6 + X_2$$
$$X_4 + X_8 + X_5 + X_1$$
$$X_5 + X_1 + X_4 + X_8$$
$$X_6 + X_2 + X_3 + X_7$$
$$X_7 + X_3 + X_2 + X_6$$
$$X_8 + X_4 + X_1 + X_5$$

68

$$X_9 + X_{10} + X_9 + X_{10}$$
$$X_{10} + X_9 + X_{10} + X_9$$

Of these combinations only three are independent; after normalization these give:

$$\psi = (c_1/2)(X_1 + X_4 + X_5 + X_8) + (c_2/2)(X_2 + X_3 + X_6 + X_7)$$

$$+ (c_3/\sqrt{2})(X_9 + X_{10})$$

The elements of the determinant are found in the usual way; for example,

$$H_{11} = \int \frac{1}{2}(X_1 + X_4 + X_5 + X_8) H \frac{1}{2}(X_1 + X_4 + X_5 + X_8)d\tau = \alpha$$

$$H_{12} = \int \frac{1}{2}(X_1 + X_4 + X_5 + X_8) H \frac{1}{2}(X_2 + X_3 + X_6 + X_7)d\tau = \beta$$

$$H_{23} = \int \frac{1}{2}(X_2 + X_3 + X_6 + X_7) H \frac{1}{\sqrt{2}}(X_9 + X_{10})d\tau = 0$$

The determinant for Γ_1 is now

$$\begin{vmatrix} \alpha - E & \beta & \beta\sqrt{2} \\ \beta & \alpha + \beta - E & 0 \\ \beta\sqrt{2} & 0 & \alpha + \beta - E \end{vmatrix} = \begin{vmatrix} x & 1 & \sqrt{2} \\ 1 & x+1 & 0 \\ \sqrt{2} & 0 & x+1 \end{vmatrix} = 0$$

and can be solved in the usual way.

Exercise 4-4

Verify the elements given above for the Γ_1 determinant for naphthalene.

Exercise 4-5

Set up the determinants for benzene using D_{2v} symmetry operations and solve for the energy levels. Calculate DE_π. Solve for the coefficients and sketch out the orbitals.

Exercise 4-6

Use group theory to solve for the energy levels of cyclobutadiene. Calculate values for DE_π, p_{ij}, $\mathcal{F}_i$, and q_i. Use Hund's rule (p. 4) to determine the proper electronic configuration.

We proceed in the same way to find the determinant corresponding to Γ_2 for naphthalene. The dot products are:

$$X_1 + X_5 - X_8 - X_4$$
$$X_2 + X_6 - X_7 - X_3$$
$$X_3 + X_7 - X_6 - X_2$$
$$X_4 + X_8 - X_5 - X_1$$
$$X_5 + X_1 - X_4 - X_8$$
$$X_6 + X_2 - X_3 - X_7$$
$$X_7 + X_3 - X_2 - X_6$$
$$X_8 + X_4 - X_1 - X_5$$
$$X_9 + X_{10} - X_9 - X_{10}$$
$$X_{10} + X_9 - X_{10} - X_9$$

The nonzero independent combinations give

$$\psi = (c_1/2)(X_1 - X_4 + X_5 - X_8)$$

$$+ (c_2/2)(X_2 - X_3 + X_6 - X_7)$$

and the determinant is

$$\begin{vmatrix} x & 1 \\ 1 & x-1 \end{vmatrix} = 0$$

Exercise 4-7

Verify the above determinant for Γ_2 of naphthalene and find the corresponding determinants for Γ_3 and Γ_4.

Exercise 4-8

Use group theory to set up determinants for the following molecules, using D_{2v} symmetry and the indicated numberings.

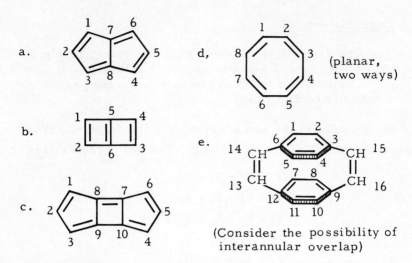

(planar, two ways)

(Consider the possibility of interannular overlap)

C₂ SYMMETRY

Relatively few π-electron problems involve molecules that permit use of D_{2v} symmetry; in fact, many substances of interest have no useable symmetry whatsoever. However, quite a few have one two-fold axis. The procedure for utilizing this is quite simple. Consider the cyclopentadienyl free radical; the five equivalent resonance forms suggest five-fold symmetry:

Unfortunately, the D_{5v} character table is rather complex, and we shall take the radical as having only a two-fold symmetry axis (c_2). Proceeding as before,

E	c_2
1	1
2	5
3	4
4	3
5	2
5	1

The character table that corresponds to these operations is

	E	c_2
Γ_1	1	1
Γ_2	1	-1

Therefore, we expect for Γ_1 $(5 \times 1 + 1 \times 1) \div 2 = $ a three-row determinant and for Γ_2 $(5 \times 1 - 1 \times 1) \div 2 = $ a two-row determinant. The wave functions are $c_1 X_1 + (c_2/\sqrt{2})(X_2 + X_5) + (c_3/\sqrt{2})(X_3 + X_4)$ and $(c_1/\sqrt{2})(X_2 - X_5) + (c_2/\sqrt{2})(X_3 - X_4)$ respectively. These give the determinants

$$\begin{vmatrix} x & \sqrt{2} & 0 \\ \sqrt{2} & x & 1 \\ 0 & 1 & x+1 \end{vmatrix} = 0 \quad \text{and} \quad \begin{vmatrix} x & 1 \\ 1 & x-1 \end{vmatrix} = 0$$

which may be solved in the usual way.

Exercise 4-9

a. Verify the determinants given above for the cyclopentadienyl radical.

b. Calculate the energy levels and DE_π for the cyclopentadienyl radical, cation, and carbanion.

72

Exercise 4-10

Using group theory, set up the determinants for

a. $\underset{1}{CH_2}=\underset{2}{CH}-\underset{3}{CH_2}\cdot$

b.

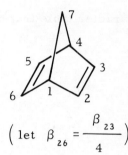

CH=CH₂

c.

d.

e.

$$\left(\text{let } \beta_{26} = \frac{\beta_{23}}{4}\right)$$

Exercise 4-11

Show how one can decide by inspection the size of determinants required for a substance with a two-fold symmetry axis.

Exercise 4-12

Calculate DE$_\pi$ for bicyclo[2.2.1]-hepta-2,5-diene (see Exercise 4-10e).

Discussion of the use of group theory involving other character tables is given by Eyring, Walter, and Kimball.[1]

[1]H. Eyring, J. Walter, and G. E. Kimball, "Quantum Chemistry", John Wiley and Sons, Inc., 1944.

Chapter 5

Aromaticity. The 4n + 2 Rule

CYCLOBUTADIENE BY THE LCAO METHOD

Application of the simple molecular orbital theory to cyclobutadiene (cf. Exercise 4-6) leads to prediction of four one-electron energy levels: $\alpha + 2\beta$, α, α, and $\alpha - 2\beta$. Use of Hund's rule leads to the following electronic configuration for the four π electrons:

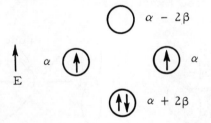

The calculated DE_π is zero. Therefore simple molecular orbital theory predicts (apparently correctly) that cyclobutadiene should have no resonance energy and, if Hund's rule is applicable, a lowest diradical (triplet) state.[1]

---

[1] In higher-order MO treatments of cyclobutadiene [cf. G. W. Wheland, Proc. Roy. Soc., 164A, 397 (1938); D. P. Craig, ibid., 202A, 498 (1950); and D. P. Craig, J. Chem. Soc., 3175 (1951)], the lowest state has all electrons paired. The reliability of these treatments is not clear. An unusual feature of the calculated lowest electron configuration is that it is not totally symmetric (i.e., it has different symmetry properties from a simple square object).

The further prediction that the dipositive ion (2π electrons) corresponding to cyclobutadiene should have paired electrons (singlet state) and a resonance energy comparable to benzene has not as yet been confirmed.

There are two further points of general interest with respect to the LCAO treatment of cyclobutadiene. First, we note that two of the molecular orbitals have the calculated energy α. Such orbitals are known as nonbonding molecular orbitals (NBMO) to distinguish them from bonding orbitals of energy $\alpha + x \cdot \beta$ (x positive) and antibonding orbitals of energy $\alpha - x \cdot \beta$ (x positive). A nonbonding molecular orbital arises because the bonding part is just cancelled by the antibonding part or because none of the atomic X functions of the molecular orbital are on adjacent carbons. The first situation would hold for the following representation of one of the cyclobutadiene NBMO, while the second is illustrated by NBMO of the allyl radical (see Exercise 3-5):

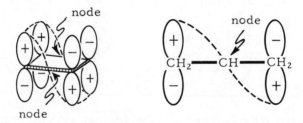

The latter case is particularly important because all odd alternant hydrocarbon radicals turn out to have a nonbonding molecular orbital.

The other point of interest about the cyclobutadiene nonbonding molecular orbitals is that they have the same energy and are thus said to be degenerate. Degenerate orbitals are more difficult to define explicitly than nondegenerate orbitals; in fact, there are an infinite number of pairs of combinations of cyclobutadiene atomic orbitals that satisfy the conditions of having energy α and giving an average of 0.5 electrons per

carbon atom (when two electrons are in the nonbonding level).
Two such combinations of degenerate orbitals are shown below,
each of which is an equally satisfactory representation:

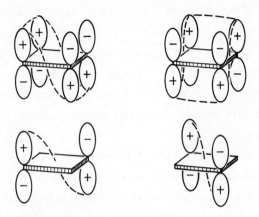

Although the electron distribution resulting from an electron
in any one of these orbitals does not have four-fold symmetry,
this symmetry does obtain for an electron distributed equally
between a pair of degenerate orbitals.

Exercise 5-1

Devise a set of degenerate orbitals for cyclobutadiene that is different from those shown above and meets
the other requirements as to energy and average electron distribution.

Exercise 5-2

Apply the simple LCAO method (use group theory)
to the cyclopropenyl cation, radical, and anion. Cal-
culate DE_π, p_{ij}, $\mathfrak{F}_i$, and q_i. Sketch out the molecular
orbitals, showing at least three different representa-
tions of the degenerate orbitals.

THE 4n + 2 RULE

E. Hückel was the first to show by the molecular
orbital theory that the monocyclic conjugated polyenes have
filled stable shells of π electrons when the number of such
electrons was 4n + 2, where n is a positive integer. When

the number is 4n, as for cyclobutadiene, the highest set of degenerate orbitals contains only two electrons and the calculated DE_π is smaller than for the 4n + 2 systems with the same value of n. This generalization is now called the 4n + 2 rule for aromatic character. It has been used with considerable success in a priori predictions of stable cyclopropenium and tropylium cations. It also explains why no one has yet been able to prepare anionic salts of cyclopropene and cycloheptatriene analogous to the stable anionic salts of cyclopentadiene.

The theoretical basis of the 4n + 2 rule should be clear through a comparison of the energy levels, electronic configurations, and delocalization energies obtained for the cyclopropenyl, allyl, and cyclopentadienyl radicals, cations, and anions (Exercises 3-5, 4-9, and 5-2) as well as cyclobutadiene and benzene (Exercises 4-5 and 4-6). The application of the rule to bridged-ring aromatic systems is generally doubtful. Some examples and further discussions are given in the paper reprinted in Appendix II.

Exercise 5-3

Sketch out qualitatively the energy levels and electronic configurations that would be expected for planar cyclooctatetraene.

Exercise 5-4

Stable cyclooctatetraene exists in the tub conformation (p. 21). Use the LCAO method (and group theory) to determine the energy levels of nonplanar cyclooctatetraene on the basis of assignment of full β for π overlap across the "double bonds" and 0.25β for overlap across the "single bonds" of the tub structure.

Exercise 5-5

Compare the π-electron energies of benzene in the delocalized cyclohexatriene configuration with alternating 1.34 and 1.54 Å bonds and the regular hexagon configuration with 1.40 Å bonds using β values appropriate for the bond distances involved (see p. 33).

Chapter 6

Molecules with Heteroatoms

THE APPLICATION of the LCAO method to other elements than carbon is straightforward as long as absolute comparisons are not required. The calculations of the electronic states of tetraazacyclobutadiene and hexaazabenzene would be exactly the same for carbon, provided the extra unshared electron pairs are regarded as being strictly localized and α and β are assigned values appropriate for nitrogen.

$$\ddot{N}{=}\ddot{N}$$
$$|\quad|$$
$$\ddot{N}{=}\ddot{N}$$

tetraazacyclobutadiene

$$\ddot{N}{=}\ddot{N}$$
$$:N \qquad N:$$
$$\ddot{N}{-}\ddot{N}$$

hexaazabenzene

That no substances of this type have yet been isolated rather diminishes the interest in calculations of this sort; however, the LCAO method has been applied to the problem of predicting the relative stabilities of configurations of a linear chain of five nitrogens $(R-N_5)$ formed by reaction of diazonium salts with azide ion.[1]

[1] J. D. Roberts, Chem. Ber., 94, 273 (1961). An English version of this manuscript is reproduced in Appendix II.

Matters become more difficult for substances that have different kinds of atoms forming π bonds because the Coulomb and resonance integrals are not the same. For example, if we wish to compare the LCAO π-electron energies of pyridine and benzene, we have to assign suitable values for $\alpha_N = \alpha_C + x\beta_{C-C}$ and $\beta_{C-N} = y\beta_{C-C}$ where x and y are parameters appropriate to pyridine.

Considerable attention has been given to LCAO calculations of the energy levels of molecules with heteroatoms, particularly heterocyclic compounds. The treatment of substances having π bonding to nitrogen, oxygen, and fluorine appears to be straightforward. Complications arise with the higher row elements because of interactions involving d orbitals. Methods of calculating π-electron energies where overlap involving d orbitals is important are available.[2] We shall be concerned here only with first-row heteroatoms. Emphasis will be on qualitative predictions based on the direction and relative magnitude of changes in DE_π, q_i, etc. resulting from heteroatom substitution. Consequently, we shall not try to achieve exact values of x and y as defined above but only values that are reasonably appropriate to the nature of the heteroatoms. An illustrative and useful table of integrals, which is at least qualitatively correct for C, N, and O, follows where α is α_C and β is β_{C-C}:

Atom	Coulomb Integral	Resonance Integral
C	α	β
N	$\alpha + \beta$	β
O	$\alpha + 2\beta$	$\beta\sqrt{2}$

[2] See, for example, H. C. Longuet-Higgins, Trans. Faraday Soc., 45, 173 (1949).

The decreases in Coulomb and resonance integrals going from carbon to nitrogen to oxygen reflect the order of increasing electronegativity. That integral values are listed for x of $\alpha + x\beta$ is less a matter of the inherent simplicity of nature than it is of ease of breaking down complex determinants.

If an atom has a formal charge, as in N-methylpyridinium ion, it would seem reasonable to use a considerably higher value of α_N than $\alpha + \beta$. For less qualitative computations it would probably be best to make appropriate corrections to the Coulomb integrals for nonself-consistent fields (see p. 60).

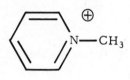

N-methylpyridinium ion

The LCAO calculations with heteroatoms proceed by the usual method. For acrolein, $CH_2=CH-CH=O$, we would have the butadiene determinant with appropriate values for α_O and β_{C-O}:

$$\begin{vmatrix} \alpha - E & \beta & 0 & 0 \\ \beta & \alpha - E & \beta & 0 \\ 0 & \beta & \alpha - E & \beta\sqrt{2} \\ 0 & 0 & \beta\sqrt{2} & \alpha + 2\beta - E \end{vmatrix} = 0$$

The energy levels would contain four π electrons, and DE_π would be calculated with the aid of E_π of the localized model from the same determinant with $H_{23} = 0$. Bond orders, $\mathfrak{F}_i$, and q values are obtained in the usual way.[*]

[*]When heteroatoms are present, E_π no longer equals $2\beta(\Sigma p_{ij}) + N\alpha$.

The most striking changes produced by heteroatoms are usually in the charge distributions. Calculations for pyrrole using the above parameters give the following charges:

$$
\begin{array}{c}
\text{CH}\!=\!\!\text{CH} \\
\text{CH}\quad\text{NH} \;\; +0.32 \\
\text{CH}\!=\!\!\text{CH} \\
-0.06 \qquad -0.10
\end{array}
$$

Exercise 6-1

Calculate DE_π, p_{ij}, $\mathcal{F}_i$, and q_i for acetyleneimine (four π electrons).

$$
\begin{array}{c}
\text{CH} \\
\| \quad\;\text{NH} \\
\text{CH}
\end{array}
$$

acetyleneimine

Compare the q_i values with those given above for pyrrole. Which substance should be the stronger base?

Exercise 6-2

How can the MO theory account for the unusually high acidity of pyrrole?

Exercise 6-3

Calculate the energy levels of azacyclobutadiene and compare them with those found earlier for cyclobutadiene.

$$
\begin{array}{c}
\text{CH} \\
\text{CH}\qquad\text{N} \\
\text{CH}
\end{array}
$$

azacyclobutadiene

Exercise 6-4

Use the simple LCAO method to make a comparison of the following π-electron systems:

a. HN=CH–CH=NH and CH_2=N–N=CH_2.

b. O=C=C=O and O=C=C=C=O.

Chapter 7

Nonplanar Systems

FREQUENTLY one is interested in nonplanar unsaturated systems such that the p orbitals are not nicely parallel to one another. No progress is possible without some way of estimating the resonance integrals. The usual way of doing this is to calculate the overlap integral S' between the orbitals of interest and use it to estimate the resonance integral β' by the relation

$$\beta' = \beta \, \frac{S'/(1 + S')}{S/(1 + S)}$$

where S and β are overlap and resonance integrals for some standard. For carbon 2p-π overlap at the ethylene distance β is the usual resonance integral and S has the value 0.28. The procedure is quite serviceable but suffers somewhat from the aesthetic dissatisfaction of assuming $S_{ij} \neq 0$ to calculate β' and then turning around and taking $S_{ij} = 0$ to get the energy levels. This dissatisfaction, of course, can be allayed by using $S_{ij} \neq 0$, but the assumption of $S_{ij} = 0$ is no worse here than in the other calculations we have discussed. Our problem is reduced to determination of S_{ij} (or S').

CALCULATION OF S_{ij}

The customary procedure for estimating S_{ij} for p orbitals that are not parallel to one another is probably best illustrated by examples. Consider first the simple case of two $2p$ orbitals whose axes lie in parallel planes at the distance r and are canted with respect to one another by the angle γ

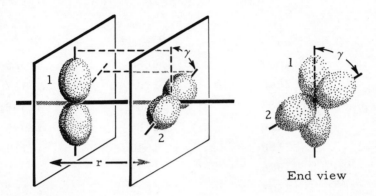

End view

For this case,

$$S_{12} = S_{\pi\pi} \cos \gamma$$

where $S_{\pi\pi}$ is the overlap integral of parallel $2p$ orbitals overlapping in the π manner at the distance r.

Exercise 7-1

Calculate the energy levels and DE_π of butadiene in a configuration at the 2,3 bond such that the planes of the double bonds lie at 60° to one another.

Values of $S_{\pi\pi}$ for $2p$ orbitals as a function of r and Z (the effective nuclear charge) have been tabulated by Kopineck.[1] A selection of these are given in Table 7-1. The effective nuclear charge for carbon $2p$ orbitals is usually taken as 3.09, and to make the data of Table 7-1 more useful for calculations involving carbon-carbon bonds, the values of r_{C-C} are listed which correspond to given values of S for $2p$ orbitals having Z = 3.09.

[1]H. J. Kopineck, <u>Z. Naturforsch.</u>, <u>5A</u>, 420 (1950).

Table 7-1

Values of $S_{\sigma\sigma}$ and $S_{\pi\pi}$ Integrals

(after Kopineck[1])

α^*	$S_{\sigma\sigma}$	$S_{\pi\pi}$	$r,^\dagger$ Å
3.0	0.1593	0.4680	1.026
3.5	.2648	.3702	1.197
4.0	.3187	.2869	1.368
4.5	.3326	.2186	1.539
5.0	.3189	.1640	1.710
5.5	.2886	.1213	1.881
6.0	.2503	.0887	2.052
6.5	.2099	.0642	2.222
7.0	.1714	.0460	2.394

*$\alpha = Zr/2a_o$, where Z is the effective nuclear charge, r the internuclear distance, and a_o the Bohr radius for hydrogen (0.5285×10^{-8} cm.).

†The internuclear distance is given for 2p-carbon orbitals (Z taken as 3.09) that correspond to the given values of $S_{\sigma\sigma}$ and $S_{\pi\pi}$.

The calculation of S_{12} is somewhat more complicated when the axes of the p orbitals lie in a plane (i.e., $\gamma = 0$) but are slanted towards one another at the angles θ_1 and θ_2 with respect to the internuclear line.

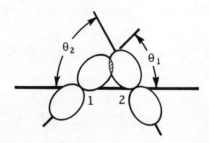

In this case we resolve the overlap into $\sigma\sigma$ and $\pi\pi$ contributions:

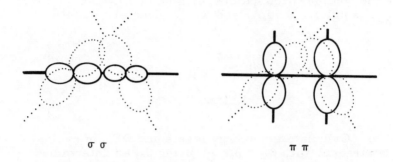

$$\sigma\ \sigma \qquad\qquad \pi\ \pi$$

Then,

$$S_{12} = S_{\sigma\sigma} \cos \theta_1 \cos \theta_2 + S_{\pi\pi} \sin \theta_1 \sin \theta_2$$

where $S_{\sigma\sigma}$ can be obtained from Kopineck's compilation[1] (see Table 7-1).

If the orbitals in addition are canted in such a way that $\gamma \neq 0$, then we can see that we should introduce the correction factor $\cos \gamma$ so that

$$S_{12} = S_{\sigma\sigma} \cos \theta_1 \cos \theta_2 + S_{\pi\pi} \sin \theta_1 \sin \theta_2 \cos \gamma$$

Exercise 7-2

Calculate S for 2p-carbon orbitals located at the 1, 4 positions of a cyclohexane ring locked into the boat form. Assume all C-C bond distances to be 1.54 Å

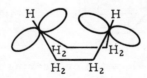

and bond angles appropriate for the state of hybridization of each carbon. Use S so obtained to calculate β for interaction between electrons in these orbitals.

86

Exercise 7-3

a. Calculate S_{23} and β_{23} for cycloöctatetraene in the tub configuration with experimental $< C\text{-}C\text{-}C = 124°$, $r_{C\text{-}C}$ (single) = 1.50 Å, and $R_{C\text{-}C}$ (double) = 1.34 Å.

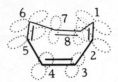

b. Calculate the energy levels and DE_π of cyclooctatetraene, with $\beta_{12} = \beta_{C\text{-}C}$, using β_{23} as determined in part (a). Use group theory to simplify the determinant (see also Exercise 5-4).

c. Calculate S_{16} and β_{16} and S_{15} and β_{15}.

d. Calculate the energy levels, DE_π, and the 1, 2 and 2, 3 bond orders of cycloöctatetraene, taking into account all at one time delocalization as measured by the "adjacent" integrals β_{12}, β_{23}, and the "cross-ring" integrals β_{15} and β_{16}.

Note that it is satisfactory to use the D_{2v} symmetry operations to simplify the secular determinant even though the tub form of cycloöctatetraene does not have D_{2v} symmetry. This is because the specified assignments of resonance integrals (except for numerical values) turn out to be just the ones we could consider for planar cyclooctatetraene as shown below:

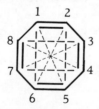

Here, the dotted lines show the cross-ring interactions.

Compare your calculated bond orders with those that correspond to the experimental bond lengths (cf. pp. 54-55.)

NONPLANAR INTERMEDIATES

By balancing calculated values of angle strain against MO delocalization energy as a function of configuration, it has been possible to predict the relative stability and geometry of some interesting postulated reaction intermediates. The calculations of Simonetta and Winstein[2] on 1, 3 interaction in homoallyl cations $\diagdown C = C - C - C \oplus$ provide an excellent example. Here the minimum overall energy was calculated corresponding to the best compromise between (1) increasing electronic stabilization coming from increasing 1, 3 overlap by bringing the 1, 3 carbons closer together and (2) decreasing stabilization associated with reducing the $< C_1 - C_2 - C_3$ (ϕ) from its normal tetrahedral value.

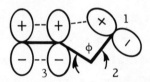

Nearly the same approach has been applied with considerable success to the 7-dehydronorbornyl cation (I)[3] and the

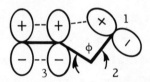

I =

alternative (and more favorable) formulation of the homoallyl cation as a bicyclobutonium ion.[4]

[2] M. Simonetta and S. Winstein, _J. Am. Chem. Soc._, 76, 18 (1954).

[3] W. G. Woods, R. A. Carboni, and J. D. Roberts, _ibid._, 78, 5653 (1956).

[4] M. E. H. Howden, Ph. D. Thesis, California Institute of Technology, 1961.

The calculations mentioned are not identical in all respects from the MO standpoint. The esoteric Simonetta-Winstein verbiage[2] almost completely conceals the use of the interesting idea that a p orbital on a sp^2-hybridized carbon connected to another carbon that has a less-than-normal bond angle will not be perpendicular to the C—C internuclear line. This idea is best illustrated by a diagram:

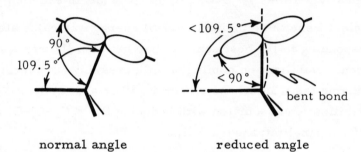

normal angle   reduced angle

The rationale is that the internuclear line should not lie in the plane determined by the sp^2-hybrid orbitals when the bond angle is less than normal because the best overlap will be obtained with a "bent" bond as indicated above by the dotted line. One way of correcting for this effect is as follows:

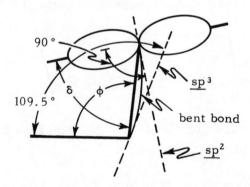

The bent bond can be taken as following a circle passing through the nuclei and tangent to the normal 109.5° direction of the sp^3 orbital. The p orbital of interest can be drawn perpendicular to the tangent of the bent-bond curve as it passes through the upper nucleus. The angle δ is then used in calculations of overlap. The effect of having $\delta < 90°$ is usually to increase the overlap integral S for a given value of ϕ. In the other reported[3,4] calculations of this type, δ was assumed to be 90°.

Exercise 7-4

Calculate separate DE_π values for the configurations (I and II) of the proposed[5] tricyclobutonium cation assuming that the CH carbon in each forms only localized σ bonds, that the C—C—C angles at the apex are 90°, and that the bond lengths are 1.54 Å.

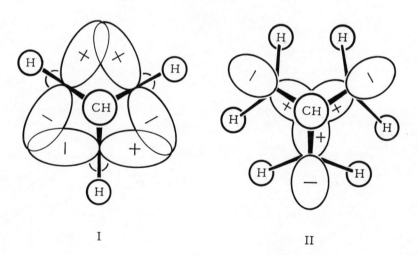

tricyclobutonium cation

I

II

[5]Cf. R. H. Mazur, W. N. White, D. A. Semenow, C. C. Lee, M. S. Silver, and J. D. Roberts, J. Am. Chem. Soc., 81, 4390 (1959) and the references cited therein.

Note that in treating I appropriate account must be taken of the fact that 2$\underline{p}$ orbitals have positive and negative lobes.

Chapter 8

Molecular Orbital Theory
and Chemical Reactivity

CHEMICAL reactivity presents one of the great unsolved problems of organic chemistry. We know a great deal about how to approach the problem but are usually stymied by the fact that we always seem to have more parameters to fix than we have results to calculate. In this chapter we shall consider contributions of the LCAO method toward predicting relative reactivities of organic molecules. We shall be illustrative rather than comprehensive, and many excellent treatments will necessarily have to be omitted to keep the discussion within reasonable bounds. Fortunately, a number of comprehensive reviews on the subject are available.

THE REACTIVITY PROBLEM

Some of the problems associated with predicting relative chemical reactivities are perhaps most easily reduced to simplest terms by considering the relative reactivities of two different positions of a given molecule toward the same reagent. The relative rates of nitration in the meta or para position of a monosubstituted benzene provide a particularly good example.

The course of aromatic nitration appears to involve rate-determining attack of $NO_2^{\oplus}$ on a ring position to give an unstable "pentadienate" cation intermediate, followed by loss of a proton to give the nitro derivative.

91

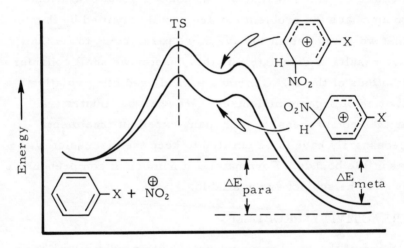

The energy profile of the course of these reactions is as follows, assuming for purposes of illustration that X favors para over meta substitution:

The rates of the reaction will be determined by the height of the energy maxima corresponding to the transition state (marked TS). The problem in calculating the energies of the transition states is the uncertainty in the degree of binding to be assigned between the $NO_2^{\oplus}$ and the ring. In the MO theory we would have to assign α and β integrals to the atoms of the partially formed bonds, thus resulting in too many parameters for any degree of confidence in the calculated transition state energies. We may proceed with fewer parameters by estimating the relative slopes of the energy curves starting up from the ground state; by calculating the energies of the intermediates; or by calculating the energy differences between the products. All of these methods will work at least qualitatively provided the energy surfaces do not cross. Unfortunately cases are known where the curves cross either before or after the transition state.

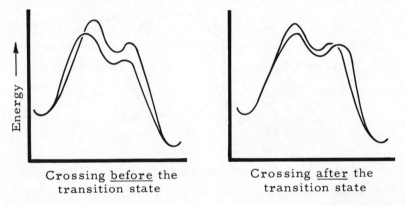

Crossing <u>before</u> the   Crossing <u>after</u> the
transition state   transition state

Conceivably the "double cross" is also a real possibility; with such a happenstance one could only rely on calculations of the relative energies of transition states.

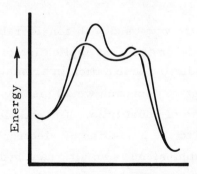

The "double cross"

We shall give one or two illustrations of calculations of reactivities based on different points in the energy profiles.

PREDICTIONS BASED ON THE GROUND STATE

In using ground state properties for predicting reactivities, we assume that the reagent will have some preference for approaching a particular site even before it gets close enough to seriously perturb the molecule through a significant degree of bond formation.

Consider azulene, which has the following "molecular diagram":

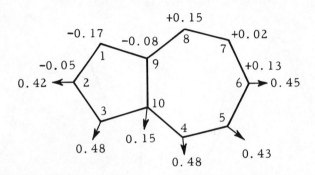

Clearly an electrophilic reagent would be expected to react at position 1 and nucleophilic reagents at positions 4 or 6. If free valence indexes are a reliable index of reactivity, either positions 3 or 4 should be most reactive toward neutral free radicals. These predictions are rather well in accord with experiment.

This procedure was used with considerable success by Wheland and Pauling[1] in the first application of molecular orbital theory to predicting orientation in aromatic substitution.

The ground state approach would clearly fail to account for the greater ease of substitution of naphthalene in the α position compared to the β position by electrophilic reagents. This is because naphthalene is an alternant hydrocarbon and is predicted to have equal charges at each π-electron center.

[1]G. W. Wheland and L. Pauling, J. Am. Chem. Soc., 57, 2086 (1935).

PERTURBATION METHODS

One possible approach to more reliable predictions of relative reactivities is to consider a point on the energy profile, such that the bond formation has occurred sufficiently with the attacking reagent to cause a considerable perturbation of the ground state, and see what energy changes the perturbation produces for the reaction paths being compared.

Thus, for nitration, we might consider what happens as $NO_2^{\oplus}$ approaches the ith position of an aromatic ring. One

possibility is that $NO_2^{\oplus}$ perturbs the system by changing the Coulomb integral of the ith position. Thus we might consider the relative effect on E_π of changing the Coulomb integral of various positions of attack. It can be shown[2] that

$$\left(\frac{\partial E_\pi}{\partial \alpha_i} \right)_{\beta_{ij}} = q_i \cdot const$$

Thus if the resonance integrals of the ith carbon to its neighbors remain constant, the change in E_π corresponding to changes in α_i are predicted to be proportional to the charge q_i on the ith carbon. This extends our confidence in q_i as a measure of reactivity since q_i will give the same answer for the reagent that is close enough to give considerable perturbation, as well as when the reagent is too far away to cause any significant perturbation.

[2] C. A. Coulson and H. C. Longuet-Higgins, Proc. Roy. Soc., 191A, 39 (1947).

For a neutral, free-radical reagent we might expect that as the reagent begins to bond to the ith position it will not change α_i but would primarily tend to change the resonance integrals β_{ij} of the ith carbon with its neighbors. This would happen because, as bonding to the radical occurs, the ith atom is on its way to becoming a saturated atom incapable of forming π bonds.

For this situation it has been shown[2] that

$$\left(\frac{\partial E_\pi}{\partial \beta_{ij}} \right)_{\alpha_i} = \text{const.} - \mathscr{F}_i \cdot \text{const.}$$

Thus, we see that the free valence index of the ith position is meaningful when a radical reagent produces a perturbation of β_{ij} as well when it is far away.

The use of q_i to evaluate changes in E_π with changes produced in α_i by polar reagents does not solve the problem of predicting the relative position of attack on alternate hydrocarbons such as naphthalene or butadiene. One rather successful approach to these substances is provided by the "frontier electron" method.[3] Here an electrophile is regarded as attacking the electrons of the highest filled orbital at the point of highest electron density.

For butadiene, the orbitals have the following electron densities (Nc_i^2, see p. 58):

One-electron energies	N	Position			
		1	2	3	4
$\alpha + 0.62\beta$	2	0.363	0.138	0.138	0.363
$\alpha + 1.62\beta$	2	0.138	0.363	0.363	0.138

[3] K. Fukui, T. Yonezawa, C. Nagata, and H. Shingu, J. Chem. Phys., 22, 1433 (1954); K. Fukui, T. Yonezawa, and C. Nagata, ibid., 26, 831 (1957).

The electron density of the highest filled orbital (frontier-electron density) is greatest at C-1 and C-4; therefore, these are predicted to be the positions most readily attacked by electrophilic reagents.

For attack by nucleophilic reagents, one can consider that the attacking reagent will tend to place a pair of electrons in the lowest unoccupied molecular orbital (frontier orbital). The position of attack is postulated to be at that atomic orbital of the frontier MO that has the largest value of c_i^2.

For butadiene, the lowest unoccupied orbital has the wave function $\psi_3 = 0.6015X_1 - 0.3717X_2 - 0.3717X_3 + 0.6015X_4$. The frontier orbital approach predicts, therefore, that nucleophilic attack on butadiene should occur at the 1 and 4 positions.

Free radical substitution has been treated in the same framework by calculating electron densities corresponding to having one frontier electron in the normally highest occupied MO and the other frontier electron in the lowest unoccupied MO. Again, for butadiene, we would predict preferential reactivity for the 1 and 4 positions because $(c_1^2)_{\psi_2} + (c_1^2)_{\psi_3} > (c_2^2)_{\psi_2} + (c_2^2)_{\psi_3}$.

A variety of calculated frontier electron and frontier orbital densities have been compiled by Fukui and co-workers.[3]

Exercise 8-1

Use the frontier approach to calculate the most favorable positions for electrophilic, nucleophilic, and free radical attack (not substitution) for

    a.   the 1 and 5 positions of "butalene"

           butalene

    b.   bicyclobutadiene

    c.   azacyclobutadiene

Other perturbation approaches to the reactivity of alternant hydrocarbons, such as naphthalene, have been discussed
by Wheland and Pauling[1] and by Coulson and Longuet-Higgins.[2]

LOCALIZATION PROCEDURES

The diagram on p. 92 of the energy profile for aromatic
nitration shows a reaction intermediate, the pentadienate
cation, as having nearly the same energy as the transition
state. If this is actually the case then the intermediate should
be very similar to, and a good model for, the transition state.
Furthermore, since the LCAO method is readily applicable to
calculation of the relative π-electron energies of intermediates
of this type, we might expect to have particularly favorable
conditions for a quantitative treatment of relative reaction rates.
The general approach is called the localization procedure. The
name arises because one of the π-electron centers of the ring
is reckoned as being converted to a saturated atom in the formation of the intermediate with localization of an electron pair.

Effects of a variety of X groups on the π-electron energies of the pentadienate intermediates for electrophilic, nucleophilic, and free radical reagents have been calculated by
Wheland.[4] These calculations showed that the LCAO method
can accommodate the general pattern of aromatic substitution

[4]G. W. Wheland, J. Am. Chem. Soc., 42, 900 (1942).

reactions. That a more distinctive, a priori flavor cannot be ascribed to the results is a consequence of having to assign values of α and β for heteroatoms in the directing substituent group (X). The difficulties are illustrated by the following exercises:

Exercise 8-2

Set up the determinants (use group theory where possible) for calculations of the π-electron energies of the pentadienate intermediates involved in the following reactions. Choose appropriate values of the α and β, showing the reasons for your choices.

a. Nitration of benzene, biphenyl, fluorobenzene, anisole, methyl benzoate, and toluene in the position para to the substituent.

b. Replacement of chlorine by ethoxide ion in p-chloronitrobenzene, p-chlorobenzonitrile, and p-chloro-benzotrifluoride.

Exercise 8-3

Show how the MO theory might be used to predict the effect of $(CH_3)_3N^{\oplus}$ as X on the relative rates of nitration in the meta and para positions of C_6H_5X. Compare your approach to the one used by Sixma.[5]

The Wheland calculations[4] did not include effects of ground state resonance, which certainly would be important in comparisons of reactivities between different C_6H_5X derivatives. Some rather crude but illustrative localization calculations are available[6] where ground state resonance has been taken into account.

Exercise 8-4

Calculate the localization energies (taking into account ground state resonance) for electrophilic, nucleophilic, and free radical attack on carbon in

[5]F. L. J. Sixma, Rec. trav. chim., 72, 273 (1953).

[6]J. D. Roberts and A. Streitwieser, Jr., J. Am. Chem. Soc., 74, 4723 (1952); see, also, ibid., 75, 6357 (1953).

a. cyclobutadiene and bicyclobutadiene

b. acetyleneimine and azacyclobutadiene

One might well wonder why the localization method is not used exclusively in calculations of substitution on aromatic systems. The principal reason is laziness. Calculation of E_π for a 16-atom system, such as pyrene, is considerably simplified by the D_{2v} symmetry operations to the solution of two five- and two three-row determinants. The corresponding localization calculation for attack on pyrene at the 1 position requires solution of a 15-row determinant. However, a calculation of this sort is child's play for a modern high-speed digital computer.

DELOCALIZATION PROCEDURES

In many reactivity problems the transition state might be said to be more delocalized than the ground state. Dissociation reactions, whether polar or free radical, have this character. The ionization of allyl chloride involves a change

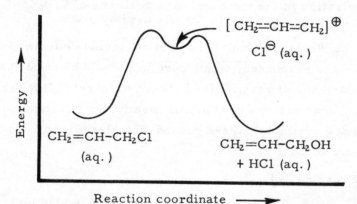

in π-electron energy of $(2\alpha + 2.828\beta) - (2\alpha + 2\beta) = 0.828\beta$ in addition to the energy changes common to those for the corresponding ionization of n-propyl chloride. Assuming that these other energy changes are the same for each chloride and that

β is the usual 20 kcal. /mole,[*] then we calculate that the
ionization of allyl chloride is some 16.5 kcal. /mole more
favorable than that of n-propyl chloride. Assuming that the
activation energy for combination of a carbonium ion with a
chloride ion is likely to be small, we can with reasonable
safety take the transition state as being close in energy to the
carbonium ion — chloride ion pair. If the 16.5 kcal. is then
assumed to reflect a difference in activation energy, the calculated factor on the ionization rate is about 10^{12}. The experimental rate difference is not known — no bonafide ionization rate is available for n-propyl chloride; however, the
calculated difference is by no means absurd.

Similar considerations may be applied to free radical
dissociation processes. The bond dissociation energies of
allyl and ethyl iodides are listed[7] as 36 kcal. and 51 kcal.
respectively. The argument used above for the allyl cation
predicts a 16.5 kcal. difference, which is almost suspiciously
close to the experimental value.

Among the many illustrative applications of the delocalization procedure to reaction rates and equilibria, the
Streitwieser[8] calculations of the relative energies of ionization of substituted triphenylmethyl chlorides are classic.
Agreement with experiment was good, and it was shown by the
LCAO method (25-row determinant) how a meta-phenyl substituent could act to suppress ionization by stabilizing the
chloride more than the cation.

[*]This is probably not a good value for carbonium ions
(or carbanions) because of nonself-consistent fields and uncertainties with respect to the overall interelectronic repulsion effects.

[7]T. L. Cottrell, "The Strengths of Chemical Bonds,"
p. 278, Academic Press, New York, 1954.

[8]A. Streitwieser, J. Am. Chem. Soc., 74, 5288 (1952).

Exercise 8-5

Use the LCAO method to predict the relative ease of reaction of the following substances in processes where the C—X bond is broken to give cationic, free radical, and anionic intermediates:

$$CH_2=CH-CH_2X$$

PRODUCT STABILITIES

Frequently one may be interested in whether or not reactivities are in accord with product stabilities. Diels-Alder additions involving aromatic compounds as dienes are of special interest in this connection. Consider the addition of maleic anhydride to benzene and anthracene. For benzene

$E_\pi = 6\alpha + 8\beta$

$E_\pi = 4\alpha + 4\beta$

the calculated change in E_π (ΔE_π) is $2\alpha + 4\beta$. The corresponding reaction for anthracene at the 9, 10 positions has $\Delta E_\pi = 2\alpha + 3.32\beta$ and, at the 1, 4 positions $2\alpha + 3.64\beta$:

$E_\pi = 14\alpha + 19.32\beta$

$E_\pi = 12\alpha + 15.68\beta$

$E_\pi = 12\alpha + 16\beta$

Clearly, addition to the 9, 10 positions of anthracene is predicted to be the most favorable, in agreement with experiment.

In many cases the most favorable sites for additions of
this type can be found by comparing sums of pairs of $\mathcal{F}_i$ values
for products of comparable likelihood on steric grounds. These
give the correct answer for anthracene, which has $\mathcal{F}_i$ = 0.520
at the 9, 10 positions and 0.459 at the 1, 4 positions. This approach provides us with an example of the crossing of energy
profiles. Consider the addition of maleic anhydride to biphenylene. The molecular diagram shows the highest sum of
$\mathcal{F}_i$ values for 1, 4 positions, yet the product stabilities indicate
that 2, 11 addition should be favored.

The following exercise illustrates how the localization procedure can be employed to determine whether crossing is likely
to occur before or after the transition state.

Exercise 8-6

On the assumption that the Diels-Alder reaction
involves a diradical intermediate (i. e. , localization),
which is close in energy to the transition state, determine whether the potential energy profile for the addition of maleic anhydride to biphenylene occurs before
or after the transition state. Note that for 2, 11 attack
two different biradicals can be formed depending upon
the position at which localization occurs.

An excellent review on the reactivity problem has been provided by Brown, [9] and a searching critique of the application of simple MO theory to prediction of reactivities has been published by Coulson and Dewar. [10]

[9] R. D. Brown, Quarterly Reviews, 6, 63 (1952).

[10] C. A. Coulson and M. J. S. Dewar, Disc. Faraday Soc., 2, 54 (1947).

Chapter 9

Approximate Methods

ALTHOUGH many very interesting calculations pertaining to structure and reactivity can be carried out with a desk calculator (particularly if group theory is used), it is often desirable to have simpler methods available at one's finger tips. An elegant approximate approach with the simplicity of a slide rule has been developed by Dewar[1] on groundwork laid by the studies of Longuet–Higgins regarding the properties of nonbonding molecular orbitals (NBMO).

NONBONDING MOLECULAR ORBITALS

Every alternant conjugated hydrocarbon with an odd number of π-electron centers has a NBMO. The bonding and antibonding orbitals have energies symmetrically disposed with respect to the nonbonding level. For the benzyl radical the energy levels are as shown on the next page. We see that the NBMO is the orbital where those electrons go that determine whether we have a benzyl cation, radical, or anion. Furthermore, since the orbital is nonbonding, DE_π will be the same for each of these species (at least in so far as the same α and β values are applicable to each).

[1]M. J. S. Dewar, J. Am. Chem. Soc., 74, 3341–3357 (1952).

Energy

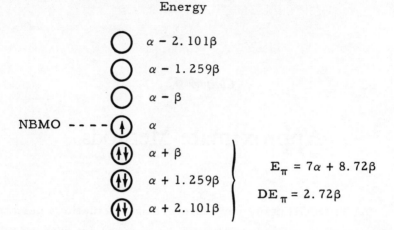

$$\alpha - 2.101\beta$$
$$\alpha - 1.259\beta$$
$$\alpha - \beta$$

NBMO - - - - α

$$\alpha + \beta$$
$$\alpha + 1.259\beta$$
$$\alpha + 2.101\beta$$

$$E_\pi = 7\alpha + 8.72\beta$$
$$DE_\pi = 2.72\beta$$

We know (see p. 60) that an alternant hydrocarbon (AH) has a self-consistent field so that $q_i = 0$ at all atoms; therefore if we remove an electron from the NBMO to get a benzyl cation, the positive charge will be distributed solely over those atoms whose orbital coefficients are not zero for the NBMO. The same will be true if we add an electron to the radical and make the benzyl anion. The NBMO coefficients are clearly of signal importance since their values determine the calculated distribution of the odd electron in the radical and the charges in the cation and anion. For the benzyl radical the NBMO may be rendered schematically as follows:

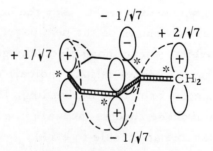

The coefficients have nonzero values for the orbitals located on the starred (p. 74) atoms provided we star four and not three atoms.

The squares of the coefficients give the electron density in the NBMO, so that 4/7 of the odd electron of the radical is predicted to be at the CH_2 group and 1/7 each at the ortho and para positions. From the argument given above, the same fractions should represent the charge distributions of the cation and anion.

It turns out to be very easy to get the coefficients of the NBMO. First, the atoms are starred to get the largest number of starred positions:

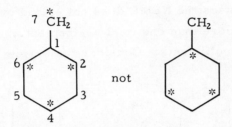

Second, we use the rule "The sum of the coefficients of the atomic orbitals of the starred atoms directly linked to a given unstarred atom is zero." Thus, the sum of c_2 and c_4 (both attached to the unstarred atom 3) must be zero. The same is true for c_4 and c_6. Similarly, $c_2 + c_6 + c_7 = 0$ since these are for the orbitals attached to the unstarred atom c_1.

Having

$$c_2 + c_4 = 0$$
$$c_6 + c_4 = 0$$
$$c_2 + c_6 + c_7 = 0$$

we find that, if we set $c_4 = 1$, then $c_2 = c_6 = -1$ and $c_7 = 2$. These coefficients are not normalized, and with the normalization factor of $1/\sqrt{7}$, we obtain

$$\psi_4 = \frac{1}{\sqrt{7}} (-X_2 + X_4 - X_6 + 2X_7)$$

Exercise 9-1

Determine the NBMO coefficients for the following radicals:

a. allyl

b. cyclobutadienylcarbinyl

c. 2, 4, 6-heptatrienyl

d. α-naphthylcarbinyl

e. triphenylmethyl

The coefficients obtained in this way are not approximate; they are the coefficients that also come out of the solution of the secular determinant.

In some cases the NBMO does not extend over the entire molecule, and more than one trial assignment must be used to get the proper coefficients. Consider the system

$$c_6 + c_8 = 0 \qquad c_{10} + c_{12} = 0 \qquad c_2 + c_{12} + c_{14} = 0$$
$$c_4 + c_6 = 0 \qquad c_4 + c_8 + c_{12} = 0 \qquad c_2 + c_4 + c_{15} = 0$$
$$c_8 + c_{10} = 0$$

Now, if we set $c_6 = 1$, then $c_4 = c_8 = c_{12} = -1$. This, however, violates the condition that $c_4 + c_8 + c_{12} = 0$. Evidently, $c_4 = c_8 = c_{12} = 0$; thence, setting $c_2 = 1$, $c_{14} = c_{15} = -1$ so that $\psi_{NBMO} = 1/\sqrt{3} (X_2 - X_{14} + X_{15})$. Clearly, the odd electron of the radical does not extend over naphthalene part of the ring system.

Exercise 9-2

a. Derive the NBMO coefficients for the following radical:

b. Calculate ΔE_π for the formation of this radical from

and compare the calculated value with ΔE_π for the corresponding process with the double bond at the 4 position saturated.

Exercise 9-3

Use the NBMO of the benzyl radical to predict which of the following would have the more basic nitrogen atom:

or

Exercise 9-4

Consider substitution of a given electron-donating group on the β-naphthylcarbinyl cation. Use the NBMO of the cation to predict qualitatively the order of stabilization that would be produced as a function of position of substitution of the electron-donating group.

Exercise 9-5

a. Determine the NBMO coefficients of

b. Predict qualitatively as much as you can about the properties of the following azaderivatives:

APPROXIMATE CALCULATIONS OF E_π

The NBMO coefficients can be used in approximate calculations of π-electron energies by a method developed by Dewar[1,2] and by Longuet-Higgins.[2] Consider a conjugated hydrocarbon (RS) with an even number of carbons and a π-electron system that might be considered to be the result of joining up two odd AH radicals (R and S) by one or more π bonds. The π-electron system of butadiene would be the result of linking up the π systems of allyl and methyl, while benzene would result from pentadienyl and methyl or two allyls.

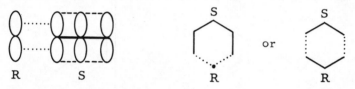

The E_π of RS might be expected to be related to the product of the coefficients of the atomic orbitals of R and S at the point of joining up; the larger the coefficients the more bonding to be expected. Dewar and Longuet-Higgins specifically propose that the NBMO coefficients may be used for this purpose with the aid of the following equation:

$$E_{\pi_{RS}} = 2\beta(\Sigma c_{o_R} \cdot c_{o_S}) + E_{\pi_R} + E_{\pi_S}$$

Here, c_{o_R} and c_{o_S} refer to the NBMO coefficients of R and S at the junction points of π-electron systems. For butadiene, we have

$$E_2 = 2\beta(1 \cdot 1/\sqrt{2}) + \alpha + 3\alpha + 2.818\beta$$
$$= 4\alpha + 4.23\beta$$

which is to be compared to $4\alpha + 4.472\beta$ for the complete calculation (p. 46). The agreement is not too good; but assuming

[2]M. J. S. Dewar, J. Chem. Soc., 329 (1950); 3532, 3534 (1952); M. J. S. Dewar and H. C. Longuet-Higgins, Proc. Roy. Soc., 214A, 482 (1952).

that a table of E_π values for simple odd AH radicals is available, such as follows, the calculations can at least be made very quickly:

Radical	E_π (by LCAO method)
Allyl	$3\alpha + 2.818\beta$
Pentadienyl	$5\alpha + 5.46\beta$
Heptadienyl	$7\alpha + 8.05\beta$
Nonadienyl	$9\alpha + 10.63\beta$
Benzyl	$7\alpha + 8.72\beta$
α-Naphthylcarbinyl	$11\alpha + 14.49\beta$
β-Naphthylcarbinyl	$11\alpha + 14.27\beta$

The two ways of assembling benzene give different calculated values of E_π.

$$E_\pi = 2\beta\left(1 \cdot \frac{1}{\sqrt{3}} + 1 \cdot \frac{1}{\sqrt{3}}\right)$$

$$+ \alpha + 5\alpha + 5.46\beta$$

$$= 6\alpha + 7.77\beta$$

$$E_\pi = 2\beta\left(\frac{1}{\sqrt{2}} \cdot \frac{1}{\sqrt{2}} + \frac{1}{\sqrt{2}} \cdot \frac{1}{\sqrt{2}}\right)$$

$$+ 2(3\alpha + 2.82\beta)$$

$$= 6\alpha + 7.63\beta$$

The agreement with the $6\alpha + 8\beta$ value obtained by the regular LCAO method is not very impressive, and there is an ambiguity about which way to build up the system. It will be shown later how this ambiguity can be turned to real advantage in another connection. The best choice of R and S is expected on theoretical grounds to be the one that gives the smallest product $(\Sigma c_{o_R} c_{o_S})$ since this corresponds to the smallest perturbation.[1]

The Dewar method in at least one case may give a more realistic answer than more refined calculations. Pentalene (as yet unsynthesized) is predicted by LCAO calculations to have $E_\pi = 8\alpha + 10.46\beta$ and $DE_\pi = 2.46\beta$. The approximate method gives $E_\pi = 8\alpha + 8.05\beta$ and $DE_\pi = 0.05\beta$.

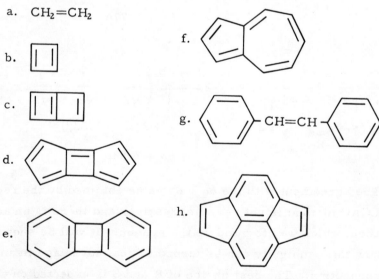

pentalene

$$E_\pi = 2\beta\left(1 \cdot 0 + 1 \cdot \frac{1}{2} - 1 \cdot \frac{1}{2}\right) + \alpha + 7\alpha + 8.05\beta$$

$$= 8\alpha + 8.05\beta$$

Exercise 9-6

Estimate E_π by the RS technique of assembling the π-electron system for the following substances:

a. $CH_2{=}CH_2$

b.

c.

d.

e.

f.

g. $-CH{=}CH-$

h.

Exercise 9-7

Consider the possibility of calculating E_π of conjugated hydrocarbons by assembling their π-electron systems from R and S units where R and S are free radicals (not necessarily AH) and E_π is considered to be some function of the $\mathcal{Z}_i$ values of the radicals at the junction points.

ORIENTATION IN AROMATIC SUBSTITUTION

We have shown how the combination of the π–electron system, R and S, may lead to different approximate E_π values for a given hydrocarbon depending upon how R and S are chosen. With naphthalene, for example,

$$E_\pi = 2\beta \left(1 \cdot \frac{1}{\sqrt{11}} + 1 \cdot \frac{2}{\sqrt{11}} \right) + \alpha + 9\alpha + 11.38\beta$$

$$= 10\alpha + 13.10\beta$$

$$E_\pi = 2\beta \left(1 \cdot \frac{1}{\sqrt{8}} + 1 \cdot \frac{2}{\sqrt{8}} \right) + \alpha + 9\alpha + 10.83\beta$$

$$= 10\alpha + 12.95\beta$$

Dewar uses these differences as a way of approximating localization energies. In other words, instead of calculating the π–electron energy of naphthalene by the RS procedure, it is used to estimate the energy of the localized intermediates that corresponds to substitution at the 1 and 2 positions. The outcome is as follows (omitting the appropriate multiples of

α as correspond to attack by cationic, anionic, or radical reagents):

For substitution at the 1 position

$$\Delta E_\pi = -2\beta \left(1 \cdot \frac{1}{\sqrt{11}} + 1 \cdot \frac{2}{\sqrt{11}} \right)$$

$$= -1.81\beta$$

For substitution at the 2 position

$$\Delta E_\pi = -2\beta \left(1 \cdot \frac{1}{\sqrt{8}} + 1 \cdot \frac{2}{\sqrt{8}} \right)$$

$$= -2.12\beta$$

This method of calculating localization energies is very quick and easy, especially for complicated polycyclic alternant hydrocarbons.

Exercise 9-8

Estimate the order of ease of attack of $NO_2^{\oplus}$ on each of the positions of the following substances by Dewar's procedure:

a. benzene   c. phenanthrene

b. anthracene   d. biphenylene

Exercise 9-9

Use Dewar's method in combination with other more qualitative reasoning to estimate the relative ease of displacement of chlorine by ethoxide ion for the monochloroquinolines and the monochloroisoquinolines.

Chapter 10

Higher Order Calculations

MOLECULAR orbital calculations of the type described in these Notes are often called zero-order calculations because of the many assumptions involved. Higher order approaches are available in considerable profusion. Unfortunately, most of these are not very convenient for use by organic chemists. It is not difficult to include overlap (i. e., take $S_{ij} \neq 0$) and make corrections in Coulomb integrals for nonself-consistent fields, in resonance integrals for bond lengths, and in the σ-bond framework for angle strain. All of this may or may not constitute a first-order approach, depending upon one's point of view.

There are some fundamental approximations in the simple LCAO method that are harder to evaluate. One is the validity of the linear combination of atomic orbitals as an approximation to molecular orbitals. Another is the assumption of localized σ bonds. A proper treatment probably should take account of the so-called σ-π interactions. Beyond these rather basic assumptions is the bothersome business of dealing explicitly with interelectronic repulsions. These repulsions are expected to be functions of molecular geometry as well as the degree of self-consistency of the molecular field. Thus, cyclobutadiene must have considerably greater interelectronic repulsion than butadiene, with the same number of π electrons.

The usual procedures for calculating interelectronic repulsions in molecules are complicated. Space does not permit discussion of more than the elements of one, perhaps typical, approach, which is of interest here because it starts with our regular LCAO molecular orbitals calculated as desired with or without overlap.

The steps involved are, first, calculation of the one-electron molecular orbital energies for the field of the nuclei and σ-bond electrons. Usually much more detailed account is taken of molecular geometry than is done in the simple MO theory. The repulsions between the electrons in the same and different molecular orbitals are then calculated for particular electronic configurations (such as the lowest state). The usual MO coefficients are used to determine the fraction of the time a given electron spends in a particular orbital. The exclusion principle is employed to reject all terms that amount to having two electrons with the same spin in a given atomic orbital. The result is to have the total π-electron energy (attraction and repulsion) of a configuration set up on the basis of one-electron molecular orbitals that were obtained without consideration of interelectronic repulsion. It would, of course, be only a coincidence if this energy were to represent the minimum possible calculated energy. The energies of a number of "excited" configurations with one, two, or several electrons in normally unoccupied molecular orbitals are also calculated. These excited states may have more or less interelectronic repulsion than the presumed lowest state.

The next step is to use the variation method to find the most favorable linear combination of the wave functions (Ψ_n), corresponding to particular electronic configurations, just as before we made linear combinations of atomic orbitals:

$$\Psi_o = c_1 \Psi_1 + c_2 \Psi_2 + \ldots$$

Here advantage is taken of the possibility of mixing configurations having low-energy orbitals but high interelectronic repulsion with configurations having less favorable orbitals but less interelectronic repulsion. In effect, the electrons are assumed to achieve a measure of correlation to diminish interelectronic repulsion. This procedure is called configuration interaction. Configurations with different symmetries, as judged by group theory and with different numbers of paired electrons, are found not to mix. The configuration interaction approach has been used with considerable success in correlating electronic spectra. So far it does not seem to have been applied extensively to reactivity problems, and these would be extremely laborious with a desk calculator. Hopefully, the advent of large digital computers will permit more work along these lines.

Solutions of Typical Exercises
in the Use of the
Simple LCAO Method

EXERCISE 2-8

Calculate by the LCAO MO method whether the linear (H–H–H$^{\oplus}$) state or the triangular state of $H_3^{\oplus}$ is the more stable. Do the same for H_3 and $H_3^{\ominus}$

Procedure. — The first step is to compute the energy of the molecular orbitals for each geometric arrangement. For linear $H_3^{\oplus}$ (H–H–H, atoms labeled 1 2 3), the determinant will be

$$\begin{vmatrix} \alpha - E & \beta & 0 \\ \beta & \alpha - E & \beta \\ 0 & \beta & \alpha - E \end{vmatrix} = 0$$

if it is assumed that $H_{11} = H_{22} = H_{33} = \alpha$; $H_{12} = H_{23} = \beta$; and $H_{13} = 0$. We then may write

$$\begin{vmatrix} x & 1 & 0 \\ 1 & x & 1 \\ 0 & 1 & x \end{vmatrix} = 0$$

$$x^3 - 2x = 0$$

$$x = 0$$

$$x = \pm \sqrt{2}$$

$$E = \alpha + \beta\sqrt{2}, \ \alpha, \ \alpha - \beta\sqrt{2}$$

With two electrons in the lowest orbital, we have the configuration

$\alpha - \beta\sqrt{2}$

α

$\left.\begin{array}{c} \\ \\ \\ \\ \end{array}\right\}$ $E = 2\alpha + 2.83\beta$

$\alpha + \beta\sqrt{2}$

For H_3 we have one more electron and $E = 3\alpha + 2.83\beta$. For
$H_3^{\ominus}$ and still another electron $E = 4\alpha + 2.83\beta$.

Proceeding in the same way for $H_3^{\oplus}$ in the triangular
configuration, the determinant is found to be

$$\begin{vmatrix} \alpha - E & \beta & \beta \\ \beta & \alpha - E & \beta \\ \beta & \beta & \alpha - E \end{vmatrix} = 0$$

where $H_{11} = H_{22} = H_{33} = \alpha$ and $H_{12} = H_{13} = H_{23} = \beta$. We can now
write

$$\begin{vmatrix} x & 1 & 1 \\ 1 & x & 1 \\ 1 & 1 & x \end{vmatrix} = 0$$

$$x^3 - 3x + 2 = 0$$
$$x = +1, +1, -2$$
$$E = \alpha + 2\beta, \ \alpha - \beta, \ \alpha - \beta$$

With two electrons in the lowest orbital, we have the configuration

○   ○ $\alpha - \beta$

$$E = 2\alpha + 4\beta$$

(↑↓) $\alpha + 2\beta$

For H_3, the energy of the triangular configuration is $3\alpha + 3\beta$;
while, for $H_3^{\ominus}$, it is $4\alpha + 2\beta$.

We see that the triangular state of $H_3^{\oplus}$ is predicted by
the simple LCAO method to be more stable than the linear
state. However, the reverse order of stabilities is suggested
for $H_3^{\ominus}$. The two states are predicted to have nearly equal
energies for H_3.

EXERCISES 2-14, 3-1, 3-3, and 3-4

Calculate the π-energy levels, DE_{π}, the final wave
functions, p_{ij}, $\mathfrak{F}_i$, and q_i for bicyclobutadiene.

Procedure. — The π-electron system of bicyclobutadiene
is as shown below:

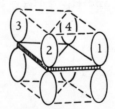

Proceeding as for 1,3-butadiene, we set $H_{11} = H_{22} = H_{33} = H_{44}$
$= \alpha$, $H_{12} = H_{14} = H_{23} = H_{24} = H_{34} = \beta$, and $H_{13} = 0$. The determinant is shown on the next page followed by the electronic
configuration:

$$\begin{vmatrix} \alpha - E & \beta & 0 & \beta \\ \beta & \alpha - E & \beta & \beta \\ 0 & \beta & \alpha - E & \beta \\ \beta & \beta & \beta & \alpha - E \end{vmatrix} = 0$$

or

$$\begin{vmatrix} x & 1 & 0 & 1 \\ 1 & x & 1 & 1 \\ 0 & 1 & x & 1 \\ 1 & 1 & 1 & x \end{vmatrix} = 0$$

$$x[x^3 - 5x + 4] = 0$$
$$x = 0, \ 1, \ -2.5615, \ +1.5616$$

$\alpha - 1.5616\beta$

$\alpha - \beta$

α } $E_\pi = 4\alpha + 5.12\beta$

$\alpha + 2.5615\beta$

Localized bicyclobutadiene is easily calculated to have
a π-electron energy of $4\alpha + 4\beta$. The predicted resonance
energy (DE_π) is thus 1.12β (~ 20 kcal.).

For calculation of the coefficients of the ψ functions, we need to take ratios of cofactors (see p. 34). If we let $A_n =$ (cofactor)$_n$, then

$$A_1 = \begin{vmatrix} x & 1 & 1 \\ 1 & x & 1 \\ 1 & 1 & x \end{vmatrix} = x^3 - 3x + 2$$

$$A_2 = - \begin{vmatrix} 1 & 1 & 1 \\ 0 & x & 1 \\ 1 & 1 & x \end{vmatrix} = -x(x - 1)$$

$$A_3 = \begin{vmatrix} 1 & x & 1 \\ 0 & 1 & 1 \\ 1 & 1 & x \end{vmatrix} = 2(x - 1)$$

$$A_4 = - \begin{vmatrix} 1 & x & 1 \\ 0 & 1 & x \\ 1 & 1 & 1 \end{vmatrix} = -x(x - 1)$$

$$\frac{c_1}{c_1} = 1$$

$$\frac{c_2}{c_1} = \frac{-x(x - 1)}{x^3 - 3x + 2} = - \frac{x}{x^2 + x - 2}$$

$$\frac{c_3}{c_1} = \frac{2(x - 1)}{x^3 - 3x + 2} = \frac{2}{x^2 + x - 2}$$

$$\frac{c_4}{c_1} = - \frac{x(x - 1)}{x^3 - 3x + 2} = - \frac{x}{x^2 + x - 2}$$

For $E = \alpha + 2.5615\beta$, $x = -2.5615$,

$$\frac{c_2}{c_1} = \frac{-(-2.5615)}{(-2.5615)^2 - 2.5615 - 2} = 1.28075$$

$$\frac{c_3}{c_1} = \frac{2}{2} = 1$$

$$\frac{c_4}{c_1} = 1.28075$$

The ratios of coefficients must be normalized (p. 35):

$$N = (1^2 + 1.28075^2 + 1^2 + 1.28075^2)^{1/2}$$

$$= \sqrt{5.28065} = 2.29797$$

$$c_1 = \frac{1}{2.29797} = 0.43516$$

$$c_2 = \frac{1.28075}{2.29797} = 0.55733$$

$$c_3 = \frac{1}{2.29797} = 0.43516$$

$$c_4 = \frac{1.28075}{2.29797} = 0.55733$$

Therefore, for $E = \alpha + 2.5615\beta$,

$$\psi_1 = 0.43516\,X_1 + 0.55733\,X_2 + 0.43516\,X_3$$

$$+ 0.55733\,X_4$$

A check on the coefficients is provided by calculating the energy of ψ_1 through the relation,

$$E = \int \psi_1 H \psi_1 \, d\tau \Big/ \int \psi_1 \psi_1 d\tau$$

$$= \int \psi_1 H \psi_1 \, d\tau \qquad \text{(if } \psi_1 \text{ is normalized)}$$

$$E = \int (c_1 X_1 + c_2 X_2 + c_3 X_3 + c_4 X_4) H$$

$$(c_1 X_1 + c_2 X_2 + c_3 X_3 + c_4 X_4) \, d\tau$$

If we take $H_{11} = H_{22} = H_{33} = H_{44} = \alpha$, $H_{12} = H_{14} = H_{23} = H_{24} = H_{34}$ = β, and $H_{13} = 0$, then

$$E = (c_1^2 + c_2^2 + c_3^2 + c_4^2)\alpha + (2c_1c_2 + 2c_1c_4 + 2c_2c_3$$
$$+ 2c_2c_4 + 2c_3c_4)\beta$$

Using the above values of the coefficients

$$E = 0.99996\alpha + 2.5615\beta$$

which is a satisfactory check.

In the same way, $E = \alpha$ has the corresponding ψ function

$$\psi_2 = (1/\sqrt{2})(X_1 - X_3)$$

When $E = \alpha - \beta$, if we substitute $x = 1$ in the equation,

$$\frac{c_2}{c_1} = - \frac{x}{x^2 + x - 2}$$

we find $(c_2/c_1) = 1/0$, which means that c_1 (and c_3) must be equal to zero. If so, then

$$\psi_3 = (1/\sqrt{2})(X_2 - X_4)$$

For $E = \alpha - 1.5616\beta$, the usual procedure gives

$$\psi_4 = 0.55733 X_1 - 0.43517 X_2$$
$$+ 0.55733 X_3 - 0.43517 X_4$$

For the bond orders (cf. p. 53),

$$P_{ij} = \sum^{\psi_{occ.}} N c_i c_j$$

We need only consider p_{12} and p_{24}:

$$p_{12} = 2 \cdot c_1 c_{2\psi_1} + 2 \cdot c_1 c_{2\psi_2}$$
$$= 2 \cdot 0.43516 \cdot 0.55733 + 2 \cdot 0.7020 \cdot 0$$
$$= 0.48506$$

$$p_{24} = 2 \cdot 0.55733 \cdot 0.55733 + 2 \cdot 0 \cdot 0$$
$$= 0.62123$$

The bond orders can be checked by the equation (cf. p. 55)

$$E = N\alpha + 2\beta(\Sigma p_{ij})$$
$$= 4\alpha + 2\beta(4 \cdot 0.48506 + 0.62123)$$
$$= 4\alpha + 5.123\beta$$

The free valence indexes $\mathfrak{F}_i$ are calculated by the following equation (cf. pp. 56-57):

$$\mathfrak{F}_i = 4.732 - \Sigma p_{ij,\,\sigma} - \Sigma p_{ij,\pi}$$

$$\mathfrak{F}_1 = 4.732 - 3 - 2 \cdot 0.4851$$
$$= 0.762$$

$$\mathfrak{F}_2 = 4.732 - 3 - 2 \times 0.4851 - 0.6212 = 0.141$$

The charge distribution in the π-electron system can be evaluated in terms of q_i (p. 58) where

$$q_i = 1.000 - \sum^{\psi_{occ}} N c_i^2$$

For bicyclobutadiene,

$$q_1 = q_3 = 1.000 - 2(0.43516)^2 - 2(0.70715)^2$$
$$= -0.37884$$

and

$$q_2 = q_4 = 1.000 - 2(0.55733)^2 + 2(0)^2$$
$$= +0.37884$$

The above calculated quantities are summarized in the following "molecular diagram" of bicyclobutadiene:

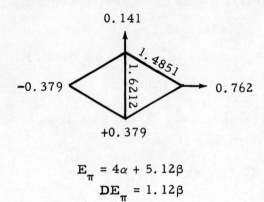

$$E_\pi = 4\alpha + 5.12\beta$$
$$DE_\pi = 1.12\beta$$

Reprints of Articles on

LCAO Calculations

[Reprinted from the Journal of the American Chemical Society, **74.** 4579 (1952).]

[CONTRIBUTION FROM THE DEPARTMENT OF CHEMISTRY AND LABORATORY FOR NUCLEAR SCIENCE AND ENGINEERING, MASSACHUSETTS INSTITUTE OF TECHNOLOGY]

Small-Ring Compounds. X. Molecular Orbital Calculations of Properties of Some Small-Ring Hydrocarbons and Free Radicals[1]

BY JOHN D. ROBERTS, ANDREW STREITWIESER, JR.,[2] AND CLARE M. REGAN

RECEIVED MARCH 17, 1952

The molecular orbital (LCAO) method has been used to calculate the electron delocalization energies, bond orders and free-valence indexes of some cyclic small-ring hydrocarbons and free radicals including a number of cyclobutadiene derivatives. It is concluded that the $(4n + 2)$ π-electron rule of aromatic stability can only be justified by the simple molecular orbital treatment for monocyclic conjugated polyolefins.

One of the substantial successes of the simple molecular orbital theory as developed by Hückel[3] is the prediction that, of the completely-conjugated planar monocyclic polyolefins as cyclobutadiene, benzene, etc., those which possess $(4n + 2)$ π-elec-

trons $(n = 0, 1, 2, 3 \ldots)$ will be peculiarly stable by virtue of having fully-filled molecular orbitals with substantial electron delocalization (resonance) energies as compared to the classical valence bond structures. The same rule may be applied[3,4] without known exceptions, to the cyclopropenyl, cyclopentadienyl, cycloheptatrienyl, etc., cations, anions and free radicals although but few quantitative cal-

(1) Supported in part by the program of research of the United States Atomic Energy Commission under Contract AT(30-1)-905.

(2) U. S. Atomic Energy Commission Post-Doctoral Fellow, 1951–1952.

(3) E. Hückel, *Z. Physik,* **70,** 204 (1931); "Grundzüge der Theorie ungesättiger and aromatischer Verbindungen," Verlag Chemie, Berlin, 1938, pp. 77-85.

(4) (a) H. J. Dauben, Jr., and H. J. Ringold, THIS JOURNAL. **73,** 876 (1951); (b) W. v. E. Doering and F. L. Detert, *ibid.,* **73,** 876 (1951).

culations[3,5] on such species have been published previously. It has been sometimes assumed[6] without proof that the $(4n + 2)$ π-electron rule holds for polycyclic as well as monocyclic conjugated polyolefins despite the fact that a number of seemingly anomalous stable substances are known; e.g., dibenzcyclobutadiene (diphenylene), acenaphthylene, pyrene, fluoranthene, etc. In the present work, the general applicability of the rule has been considered as part of a search for new cyclic conjugated systems, particularly derivatives of cyclobutadiene which might be predicted on theoretical grounds to be reasonably stable. Cyclobutadiene itself has been well studied from the standpoint of the molecular orbital theory[3,5,7] and has been predicted to have an unstable triplet ground state. Cyclobutadiene is of course highly symmetrical and it has been of interest to determine whether the simple molecular orbital theory predicts that less-symmetrical substituted cyclobutadienes would be more stable and have triplet ground states.

All of the calculations in the present paper have been made by the simple molecular orbital method[3,8,9] with neglect of resonance integrals between non-adjacent atoms and of non-orthogonality of atomic orbitals on different nuclei. Wherever possible the secular determinants were factored by group theory procedures.[9] The results must be regarded as being uncertain and essentially qualitative by virtue of the known limitations of the method, including not only the general difficulties discussed by Coulson and Dewar[10] but also the uncertainties introduced by non-self-consistent fields in other than "alternant" hydrocarbons.[11] For each compound, we have calculated the delocalization (resonance) energy (DE) in units of β (about 17 kcal.), the bond orders[8,12] and the "free-valence" indexes.[13] The results are given in Fig. 1. Where the simple molecular orbital theory predicts a triplet ground state, the compounds in

Fig. 1 are marked with a T following the figures for DE.

Compounds I–XIII are cyclobutadiene derivatives of various types. Cyclobutadiene itself (I) is predicted to have zero DE, a triplet ground state[7b,e] (cf. however, Craig[7f,g]), but not unusual free-valence indexes (F).[14] The apparent instability of the substance might be ascribed to the triplet ground state[7e] on the basis of the molecular orbital treatment since the known cyclopropene should have comparable or greater angular strain. It is interesting that various types of substituted cyclobutadienes without fused rings (II–VI) are predicted to have moderate DE-values but also triplet ground states arising from accidental degeneracies. The vinyl derivatives (II–IV) show quite high F-values at the terminal positions of the double bonds. VII–XI are benzcyclobutadienes, the calculations for which indicate clearly the lack of theoretical justification for the $(4n + 2)$ π-electron rule when applied to other than monocyclic systems. VII, VIII[15] and XI violate the rule, but are predicted to have singlet ground states, substantial DE-values (particularly for VIII which has actually been shown to be quite stable[16]) and F-figures at all positions lower than those of ethylene. On the other hand, IX which is an isomer of naphthalene with ten π-electrons is predicted to have a triplet ground state although its position isomer X should have a singlet ground state. IX is particularly interesting as an example of a possible "aromatic"[7a] "alternant"[11] hydrocarbon with a predicted triplet ground state.

Comparisons of XII and XIII with cyclobutadiene (I) are very interesting. Classical valence theory can only predict that fusion of double bonds onto I would result in considerably less stable substances. However, the simple molecular orbital treatment suggests that XII and XIII would be very different from I in having singlet ground states with substantial DE- and low F-values. If XII could be prepared,[17] studies of its bond distances would be of considerable importance since they would provide an excellent competitive test of the predictions of the simple valence bond and molecular orbital treatments. The valence bond method predicts the order of the central bond to be 1.33 corresponding to a C–C distance of about 1.42 Å. as in graphite while the molecular orbital approach, with a calculated bond order of 1.00, predicts a bond distance of about 1.54 Å. as in normal single bonds.

XIV–XVII are cross-conjugated polymethylene-substituted systems which irrespective of symmetry and number of π-electrons are predicted to

(5) G. W. Wheland, J. Chem. Phys., 2, 474 (1934).

(6) Cf., (a) V. Boekelheide, W. E. Langeland and C. T. Liu, This Journal, 73, 2432 (1951); (b) J. D. Roberts and W. F. Gorham, ibid., 74, 2278 (1952); (c) W. v. E. Doering, Abstracts of American Chemical Society Meeting, New York, September, 1951, p. 24M.

(7) (a) W. G. Penney, Proc. Roy. Soc. (London), A146, 223 (1934); (b) G. W. Wheland, ibid., A164, 397 (1938); (c) C. A. Coulson, ibid., A169, 413 (1939); (d) G. W. Wheland, This Journal, 63, 2025 (1941); (e) C. A. Coulson and W. E. Moffitt, Phil. Mag., [7] 40, 1 (1949); (f) D. P. Craig, Proc. Roy. Soc. (London), A202, 498 (1950); (g) D. P. Craig, J. Chem. Soc., 3175 (1951).

(8) C. A. Coulson and H. C. Longuet-Higgins, Proc. Roy. Soc. (London), A191, 39 (1947).

(9) H. Eyring, J. Walter and G. E. Kimball, "Quantum Chemistry," John Wiley and Sons, New York, N. Y., 1944, Chap. XIII.

(10) C. A. Coulson and M. J. S. Dewar, Discussions of the Faraday Soc., 2, 54 (1947).

(11) (a) C. A. Coulson and G. S. Rushbrooke, Proc. Camb. Phil. Soc., 36, 193 (1940); (b) D. P. Craig and A. Maccoll, J. Chem. Soc., 964 (1949); (c) Craig[7f,g] has recently indicated that neither the simple molecular orbital or valence bond treatment is likely to be reliable for calculation of the properties of cyclobutadiene or other conjugated cyclic polyolefins (designated as "pseudoaromatic" compounds) in which configuration interaction is important; (d) Prof. C. A. Coulson (private communication) suggests that in many of our small-ring examples (Fig. 1) the neglected π-π-interactions are possibly of comparable importance to the π-π-interactions.

(12) C. A. Coulson, Proc. Roy. Soc. (London), A164, 383 (1938).

(13) (a) C. A. Coulson, Trans. Faraday Soc., 42, 265 (1946); Discussions of Faraday Soc., 2, 7 (1947); J. chim. phys., 45, 243 (1948); (b) in our calculations, we need N_{max} equal to 4.732 since the value 4.698 used by Coulson gives a negative value of F for $C(CH_2)_3$.

(14) Typical calculated F-values for different types of carbon atoms are as follows: methyl radical, 1.73; α-position of a benzyl radical, 1.04; α-positions in p-quinodimethane which is apparently stable in the vapor state but which polymerizes rapidly in condensed phases, 0.92 (singlet state); cf. C. A. Coulson, D. P. Craig, A. Maccoll and A. Pullman, Discussions of the Faraday Soc., 2, 36 (1947); ethylene, 0.73; benzene, 0.23; central carbon of $C(CH_2)_3$, 0.00.

(15) VIII has been treated by the molecular orbital method previously by other workers whose calculations are given here for comparison purposes; cf. C. A. Coulson, Nature, 150, 577 (1942), and J. Waser and V. Schomaker, This Journal, 65, 1451 (1943).

(16) W. C. Lothrop, ibid., 63, 1187 (1941); 64, 1698 (1942); see also Waser and Schomaker.[15]

(17) Experiments directed toward synthesis of simple derivatives of XII are currently in progress.

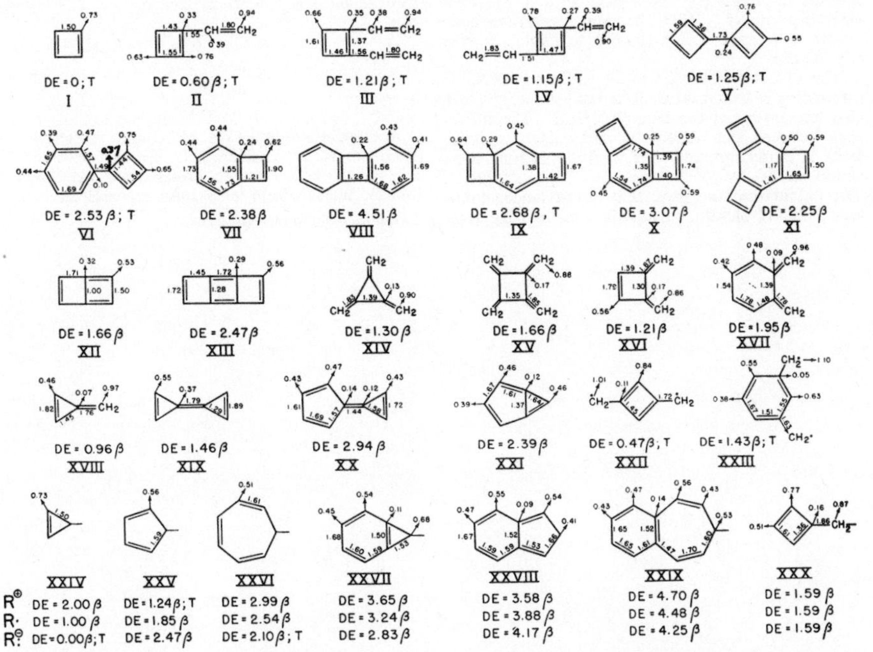

Fig. 1.—Calculations by molecular orbital method. Delocalization energies (DE) are given below each formula, the bond orders (p) are shown by figures near each bond and the free-valence indexes (F) for each position are placed at arrow points. The letter T denotes a predicted triplet ground state. The free valence indexes given for XXIV–XXX are those calculated for the free radicals.

have singlet ground states. Although the calculated DE-values[18] are substantial, the F's at the CH_2 positions are quite high and suggest that these substances should polymerize readily like p-quino-dimethane.[14]

XVIII–XXI are possible fulvene-like substances and are predicted to have singlet ground states and quite stable π-electron systems.[19,20] XX is particularly interesting since the three- and five-membered unsaturated rings might be qualitatively expected to accommodate well positive and negative charges, respectively, to give a charge distribution as in XXXI. The calculated DE is high (fulvene with an additional double bond = 2.80 β[20]) and as

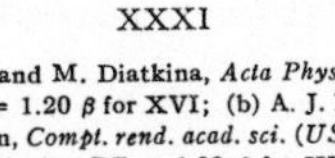

XXXI

would be expected for the postulated charge separation, the computed bond order of the bond linking the two rings is quite low compared to the corresponding bonds in XIX and fulvalene (1.67).[20] XXI has interest as a possible non-pseudoaromatic[7g] analog of azulene and pentalene with a substantial predicted resonance energy.

XXII and XXIII represent diradical isomers of XVI and XVII. Here, the molecular orbital treatment agrees with the classical valence theory in predicting that these substances should be diradicals with high F-values. Both substances have low DE's compared with their isomers.

XXIV–XXIX represent series of cyclic conjugated cations, free radicals and anions. With XXIV–XXVI, the calculated stabilities of the various ionic species alternate with ring size in a remarkable manner. It seems significant that no experimental exceptions have been found to the predicted behavior.[3,4,21] The calculations for XXVII–XXIX show that benz-substitution of XXIV–XXVI does not alter the relative ionic stability sequences predicted for the unsubstituted

(18) (a) J. Syrkin and M. Diatkina, *Acta Physiochem. (USSR)*, **21**, 641 (1946) give DE = 1.20 β for XVI; (b) A. J. Namiot, M. E. Diatkina and Y. K. Syrkin, *Compt. rend. acad. sci. (USSR)*, **48**, 233 (1945); *C. A.*, **40**, 4927 (1946) give DE = 1.92 β for XVII. In neither case were the bond orders or F-values calculated.

(19) A related molecule, fulvalene [structure], has been analyzed thoroughly by R. D. Brown, *Trans. Faraday Soc.*, **45**, 296 (1949); **46**, 146 (1950).

(20) J. Syrkin and M. Dyatkina[18] give DE = 0.96 β for XVIII.

(21) While no published evidence is available on the species corresponding to XXIV, preliminary qualitative experiments in this Laboratory indicate that cyclopropene may not react with Grignard reagents under conditions where cyclopentadiene is converted to cyclopentadienylmagnesium compounds.

species, although the differences in DE are considerably smaller. With the benz-derivatives none of the ionic species is predicted to have a lowest triplet state.

The cyclobutadienylcarbinyl radical (XXX) is interesting in that it is calculated to have a DE more than twice that of the benzyl radical. The difference between the radicals is particularly striking when it is remembered that methylcyclobutadiene would have a DE of 2 β less than that of toluene. The calculations suggest that methylenecyclobutene XXXII should be readily attacked by free-radical, anionic or cationic reagents at the 4-position.

XXXII

Acknowledgment.—We are much indebted to Professor W. G. McMillan, Jr., for advice on methods of calculation and to Professors C. A. Coulson and G. W. Wheland for helpful suggestions.

CAMBRIDGE 39, MASSACHUSETTS

Predictions of the Simple Molecular-Orbital Theory

Regarding the Flexibility of the Nitrogen Chains of Diazoazides[1]

By   John D. Roberts

Huisgen, Ugi[2] and co-workers have offered cogent evidence for formation of cyclic pentazoles (I) in the reaction of diazonium salts with azide ion. A simple (but not necessarily correct) mechanism for cyclic pentazole formation in these reactions would involve ring closure of open-chain diazoazides (II):

$$R-N_2^{\oplus} + N_3^{\ominus} \longrightarrow R-N=N-N=N=N^{\oplus\ominus} \longrightarrow R-N \begin{smallmatrix} N=N \\ | \\ N=N \end{smallmatrix}$$

II   I

Such a cyclization process might be regarded to be energetically unlikely to compete with the very rapid decomposition of II to RN_3 and N_2 because, during the ring closure, the extended chain of II would have to bend around in an almost alarming way to bring the 1- and 5-nitrogens close enough together to permit formation of an N-N σ-bond. Obviously, the ease of such bending would be influenced by the changes in conjugation between the various nitrogen atoms as the bond angles change and the purpose of this paper is to show how information can be gained from the simple (LCAO) molecular-orbital theory regarding the flexibility of diazoazide chains with the intent of assessing the ease of the cyclization reaction.

[1] Contribution No. 2555 from the Gates and Crellin Laboratories, California Institute of Technology, Pasadena, California.

[2] R. Huisgen and I. Ugi, Chem. Ber., 90, 2914 (1957) and later papers.

At first glance it might be predicted that the various resonance forms which can be written for the diazoazide chain should lead to a most favored linear structure with the chain of five nitrogens sticking out from R like a spike. Thus, consideration of the resonance forms (like IIa-IIc) suggests a hybrid structure

$$R-\overset{\oplus\ominus}{\ddot{N}}=\ddot{N}-\ddot{N}=N=\ddot{N}: \quad \longleftrightarrow \quad R-\overset{\oplus}{\ddot{N}}=N=\ddot{N}-\overset{\ominus}{\ddot{N}}=\ddot{N}: \quad \longleftrightarrow \quad R-\overset{\ominus}{\ddot{N}}-\overset{\oplus}{\ddot{N}}=N=\ddot{N}-\ddot{N}: \quad \longleftrightarrow \quad \text{etc.}$$

          IIa   IIb   IIc

with multiple-bond character between each nitrogen which would require that the chain be rather stiff. Whether the chain would be linear or not would be expected to depend on the relative contributions of each form. Thus IIa alone would lead to a molecule bent at nitrogens 1, 2 and 3 while IIb alone would lead to bends at 1, 3 and 4. This fact should warn us that the simple resonance theory might not be rigorously applicable to this variety of compound since the forms under consideration would have rather different preferred geometries when represented by conventional models.

The simple LCAO molecular-orbital treatment can be applied to the diazoazide chain in a quite straightforward way. A few simplifying assumptions made to facilitate comparisons between different configurations will be discussed as they are introduced. First, let us consider a completely linear diazoazide chain. This would have each nitrogen (except 5) forming sp-hybrid bonds to its neighbors and would give two mutually perpendicular sets of p-orbitals overlapping in the π manner (III).

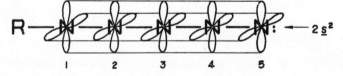

          1   2   3   4   5

III

We shall postulate atom 5 as having an unshared electron pair in a 2s-orbital, and we shall assume henceforth that such 2s-electron pairs do not interact appreciably with other electrons in 2p-orbitals on an adjacent nitrogen without first being themselves promoted to a 2p-orbital. The two mutually perpendicular sets of five p-orbitals shown for III lead by the usual procedures[3] to two sets of bonding, nonbonding, and antibonding molecular orbitals with energies and charge distributions as shown in Fig. 1(A). Throughout these calculations, we have assumed the coulomb and resonance integrals of each nitrogen to be α and β respectively (independent of hybridization and location in the chain) without any implication that α and β have the same numerical values as for carbon. To give generality, we have neglected all resonance effects of R. Also, as is customary in simple calculations, we have made no attempt to correct for nonself-consistent fields.

Of the total of twenty-five nitrogen electrons of III, nine are used in σ- bonds and two are unshared in the 2s-orbital, thus leaving fourteen electrons to be divided among the two π-orbital systems as shown in Fig. 1(A). Clearly, this electronic configuration has the appearance of being grossly unfavorable since the last two electrons must go into antibonding orbitals. In addition, the configuration would have biradical character if the spins of the two single electrons in the highest occupied orbitals are unpaired. The total π-electron energy calculated for this configuration is $14\alpha + 8.93\beta$.

Now consider a different configuration for the N_5 chain wherein we allow the N-1 to have an unshared pair so that the R-N-N angle becomes less than 180°. This arrangement leads to the hybridization scheme IV and the orbital energies and

[3] B. Pullman and A. Pullman, "Les Theories Electroniques de la Chimie Organique," Masson et Cie, Paris, 1952, pp. 176-201.

$$\underline{IV}$$

charge distributions as shown in Fig. 1(B). There are exactly the same number of
σ-bonds as for III and a total of twelve electrons to be put in the π-orbital
systems of IV. As will be seen from Fig. 1(B) the situation in one way is more
favorable than with III because there are two electrons in a less antibonding orbital
than the highest occupied orbital of III. However, there are fewer π-electrons
and less total π-bonding energy ($14\alpha + 8.93\beta$ for III vs. $12\alpha + 8.70\beta$ for IV).
Does this mean that III is $2\alpha + 0.23\beta$ more stable than IV? The answer must be no,
because we have neglected the energy change attending the conversion of N-1 from
the state where it forms linear sp σ-bonds to that where it forms angular p-bonds.
This change, of course, includes the demotion of an electron from 2p to 2s. Let us
denote the change in energy accompanying the change in hybridization of a nitrogen
of this sort as Q. Clearly Q gauges the tendency of the unshared electrons to
escape the bondage of the π-electron system. Since Q will be occurring frequently
in the subsequent calculations, we consider next how we can evaluate it or, at least,
define its limits.

Benzenediazonium ion could conceivably have its C-N-N equal to 180° (Va) or less
than 180° with a $2\underline{s}^2$ unshared electron pair on N-1 (Vb). X-ray diffraction studies[4]

[4] Chr. Rømming, Acta Chem. Scand., 13, 1260 (1959).

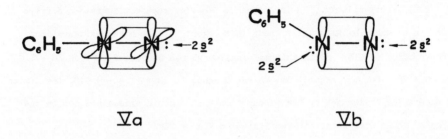

$$\underline{\text{V}}\text{a} \qquad\qquad\qquad \underline{\text{V}}\text{b}$$

indicate the linear configuration to be correct. Simple MO calculations show the energy of Va to be $4\alpha + 4\beta$ and Vb to be $2\alpha + 2\beta$. The two forms would also differ by the energy term Q associated with the change of hybridization of N-1. Since the actual configuration is linear, we deduce that $Q < (4\alpha + 4\beta) - (2\alpha + 2\beta)$ or $Q < 2\alpha + 2\beta$.

Now consider an organic azide. Here we could have the configurations VIa, VIb and VIc.

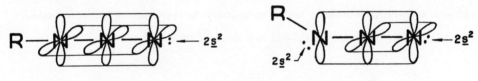

$$\underline{\text{VI}}\text{a} \qquad\qquad\qquad\qquad\qquad \underline{\text{VI}}\text{b}$$

$$\underline{\text{VI}}\text{c}$$

The calculated energies for the three forms are $8\alpha + 5.66\beta$, $6\alpha + 4.83\beta$ and $4\alpha + 2.83\beta$, respectively. In the sequence VIa–VIc, each configuration differs from its neighbor by Q.[5] It is known that organic azides have configurations corresponding to VIb.[6] With this information we can squeeze Q between $2\alpha + 0.83\beta$ and $2\alpha + 2\beta$. For the sequel, let us set Q equal to $2\alpha + (1.4 \pm 0.4)\beta$, the limits of uncertainty being set by the presumption that organic azides are not on the verge of going over either to configuration VIa or VIc.

After this lengthy detour for the purpose of evaluating Q, we return to our consideration of the diazoazide configurations III and IV. With the inclusion of Q as $2\alpha + (1.4 \pm 0.4)\beta$ as a stabilizing factor for IV, we find IV now to be more stable than III by $[2\alpha + (1.4 \pm 0.4)\beta] - (2\alpha + 0.23\beta)$ or $(1.2 \pm 0.4)\beta$. Since β for N–N bonds could well fall anywhere in the range of 10–30 kcal, IV is certainly much more favorable than III.

With the aid of the concepts developed above we can compute energies for a succession of diazoazide configurations (VII–XI) with bends at different places and with increasing bending as befits an approach to formation of a cyclic penta-zole (I). Each of the forms (VII–XI) has the same number of σ-bonds.[7]

---

[5] Note that VIc differs from VIb by only one Q unit because one of the unshared pairs on N–3 is a $2\underline{p}^2$ pair with energy 2α. Thus, N–3 undergoes no hybridization change in going from configuration VIb to VIc.

[6] L. Pauling and L. O. Brockway, J. Am. Chem. Soc., 59, 13 (1937).

[7] No attempt was made to compare the MO energy of I with those calculated for the diazoazide configurations because I has an additional σ-bond.

137

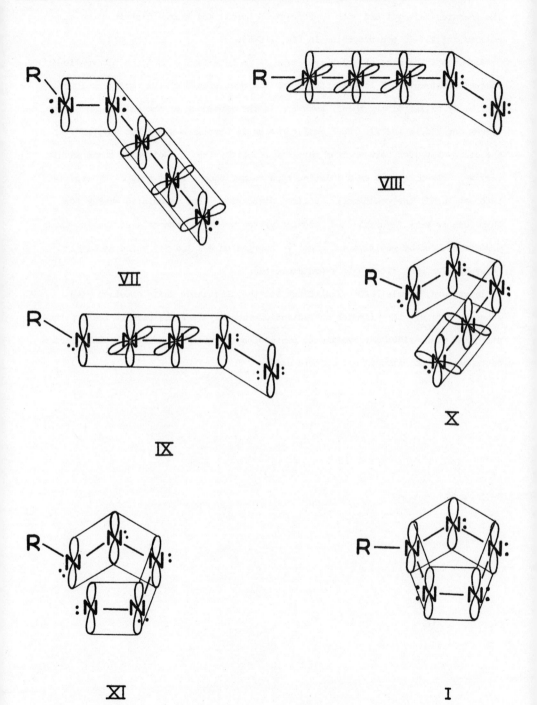

VIII

VII

IX

X

XI

I

The energies (without and with appropriate Q terms) and charge distributions calculated for VII-XI are presented in Fig. 1(C-G).

Although the limits of error are large it is interesting that the "conventional"
diazoazide structure X is predicted to be the most stable of the configurations.
The really extraordinary thing, however, is the closeness of the calculated energy
values for VII, X and XI. Each configuration is bent in a different way; and, if
the energy barriers between them were not too high, the   5-nitrogen chain might
very well resemble more an undulating rope rather than a stiff spike! Of especial
interest is XI, the practically cyclized diazoazide. The calculated energy for
this form is very favorable and, amazingly, the predicted charge distribution shows
a juxtaposition of positive and negative charges on N-1 and N-5 which is highly
favorable for ring closure to a pentazole (I).

In summary, simple LCAO calculations for the diazoazide chain combined with a
reasonable figure for nitrogen hybridization changes, lend credence to the hypothe-
sis[2] that diazoazides may cyclize to pentazoles at rates comparable to their facile
decomposition to nitrogen and organic azides.

Formula	III	IV	VII	VIII	IX	X	XI
Calculated π-electron energy	$14\alpha + 8.93\beta$	$12\alpha + 8.70\beta$	$10\alpha + 8.28\beta$	$12\alpha + 8.29\beta$	$10\alpha + 7.46\beta$	$8\alpha + 7.46\beta$	$6\alpha + 5.46\beta$
Number of Q units	0	1	2	1	2	3	4
Corrected electron energy, less 14α; $Q = 2\alpha + (1.4 \pm 0.4)\beta$	8.93β	$(10.1 \pm 0.4)\beta$	$(11.1 \pm 0.8)\beta$	$(9.8 \pm 0.4)\beta$	$(10.3 \pm 0.8)\beta$	$(11.7 \pm 1.2)\beta$	$(11.1 \pm 1.6)\beta$
Calculated charges							
N-1	-0.17	-0.33	-0.33	-0.17	-0.33	-0.33	-0.33
N-2	+0.50	+0.28	0.00	+1.00	+1.00	0.00	0.00
N-3	+0.33	+0.39	+0.17	+0.17	+0.67	-0.33	-0.33
N-4	+0.50	+0.72	+1.00	0.00	0.00	+1.00	0.00
N-5	-1.16	-1.05	-0.83	-1.33	-1.33	-0.33	+0.67

Energy levels

Antibonding:
-1.73β
-1.62β
-1.41β
-1.00β
-0.62β

Nonbonding:
α +0·β
+0.62β
+1.00β

Bonding:
+1.41β
+1.62β
+1.73β

A B C D E F G

Fig. 1(A-G)

Appendix III

General Bibliography

1. C. A. Coulson, "Valence", Oxford University Press, London, 1952.

2. L. Pauling, "Nature of the Chemical Bond", Cornell University Press, Ithaca, N. Y., 3rd ed., 1960.

3. G. W. Wheland, "Resonance in Organic Chemistry", John Wiley and Sons, Inc., New York, 1955.

4. F. O. Rice and E. Teller, "The Structure of Matter", John Wiley and Sons, Inc., New York, 1949.

5. R. Daudel, R. Lefebvre, and C. Moser, "Quantum Chemistry, Methods and Applications", Interscience Publishers, New York, 1959.

6. A. Pullman and B. Pullman, "Les Theories Electroniques de la Chimie Organique", Masson et Cie., Paris, 1952.

7. H. Eyring, J. Walter, and G. E. Kimball, "Quantum Chemistry", John Wiley and Sons, Inc., New York, 1944.

8. K. S. Pitzer, "Quantum Chemistry", Prentice-Hall, New York, 1953.

9. E. Cartmell and G. W. A. Fowles, "Valency and Molecular Structure", Academic Press, Inc., New York, 1956.

10. Y. K. Syrkin and M. E. Dyatkina, "Structure of Molecules and the Chemical Bond" (translated from Russian by M. A. Portridge and D. O. Jordan), Interscience Publishers, New York, 1950.

11. G. Olah, "Einführung in die theoretische organische Chemie", Akademie-Verlag, Perlin, 1960.

12. H. A. Staab, "Einführung in die theoretische organische Chemie", Verlag Chemie, Weinheim, 1959.

13. J. A. A. Ketelaar, "Chemical Constitution", Elsevier Publishing Co., Amsterdam, 1953.

14. A. Streitwieser, Jr., "Molecular Orbital Theory for Organic Chemists", John Wiley and Sons, Inc., New York, 1961.

15. J. W. Linnett, "Wave Mechanics and Valency", Methuen and Co., Ltd., London, 1960.

16. V. Heine, "Group Theory in Quantum Mechanics", Pergamon Press, New York, 1960.

Name Index

Alder, K. 41, 102, 103

Boekelheide, V. 128

Bohr, N. 2, 23, 84

Brockway, L. O. 136

Brown, R. D. 104, 129

Brown, W. G. 33

Carboni, R. A. 87

Cartmell, E. 140

Cottrell, T. L. 101

Coulson, C. A. 1, 14, 24, 53, 55, 56, 60, 95, 98, 104, 128, 130, 140

Craig, D. P. 73, 128

Cruickshank, D. W. J. 54

Dauben, H. J., Jr. 127

Daudel, R. 140

Detert, F. L. 127

Dewar, M. J. S. 55, 103, 104, 110, 113, 114, 128

Diels, O. 41, 102, 103

Doering, W. v. E. 127, 128

Dyatkina, M. E. 129, 140

Eyring, H. 72, 128, 140

Fowles, G. W. A. 140

Fukui, K. 96, 97

Gorham, W. F. 128

Heine, V. 141

Howden, M. E. H. 87

Hückel, E. 75, 127

Huisgen, R. 131

Hund, F. 4, 70, 73

Jordan, D. O. 140

Ketelaar, J. A. A. 140

Kimball, G. E. 72, 128, 140

Kopineck, H. J. 83, 84, 85

Langeland, W. E. 128

Lee, C. C. 89

Lefebvre, R. 140

Lewis, G. N. 6

Linnett, J. W. 141

Liu, C. T. 128

Longuet-Higgins, H. C. 78, 95, 98, 105, 110, 128

Lothrop, W. C. 128

Maccoll, A. 128

McMillan, W. G., Jr. 130

Mann, D. E. 60

Mazur, R. H. 89

Moffitt, W. E. 128

Moser, C. 140

Mulliken, R. S. 30, 33

Nagata, C. 96

Namiot, A. J. 129

Olah, G. 140

Pauli, W. 4

Pauling, L. 1, 11, 94, 98, 136, 140

Penney, W. G. 128

Pitzer, K. S. 140

Portridge, M. A. 140

Pullman, A. 128, 133, 140

Pullman, B. 133, 140

Regan, C. M. 127

Rice, F. O. 140

Rieke, C. 33

Ringold, H. J. 127

Roberts, J. D. 77, 87, 89, 99, 127, 128, 131

Robertson, A. P. 54

Rømming, C. 134

Rushbrooke, G. S. 60, 128

Schmeising, H. N. 55

Schomaker, V. 128, 130

Semenow, D. A. 89

Shingu, H. 96

Silver, M. S. 89

Simonetta, M. 87, 88

Sixma, F. L. J. 99

Slater, J. C. 11

Staab, H. 140

Streitwieser, A. , Jr. 99, 101, 127, 141

Syrkin, Y. K. 129, 140

Teller, E. 140

Ugi, I. 131

Walter, J. 72, 128, 140

Waser, J. 128

Wheland, G. W. 60, 73, 94, 98, 99, 128, 130, 140

White, W. N. 89

Winstein, S. 87, 88

Woods, W. G. 87

Yonezawa, T. 96

Subject Index

Acetylene, atomic orbital model of, 17–18

Acrolein, LCAO treatment of, 79

AH (see Alternant hydrocarbons)

Allyl radical, nonbonding orbital of, 74

    resonance energy of, 111

α (see Coulomb integral)

Alternant hydrocarbons, definition and examples of, 60

    reactivity of, 94, 96

Anthracene, calculated bond distances of, 54–55

    reactivity of, in Diels–Alder reaction, 102–103

Antibonding orbitals, 36–38

Approximate LCAO calculations, 105–114

Aromatic character, 75–76, 127–130

Atomic energy levels, 5

Atomic orbitals, use in bond formation, 6

    wave functions for, 25

Azulene, prediction of reactivity of, 94

Bent bonds, 88–89

Benzene, approximate calculation of E_π of, 104

    atomic orbital model of, 20

    bond orders of, 54

145

free valence index of, 58

resonance energy, 48

Benzenediazonium ion, LCAO treatment of, 134-135

Benzyl radical, energy levels and electronic configuration of, 106

free valence index of, 58

NBMO of, 105-107

β (see Resonance integral)

Bicyclobutadiene, LCAO treatment of, 120-126

molecular diagram of, 126

Bicyclobutonium cations, 87

Biphenylene, calculated reactivity of, in Diels-Alder reaction, 103

Bond angles, of acetylene, 18

of ethylene, 42-43

and overlap integrals, 88-89

with p orbitals, 8

prediction of, 9

of sp orbitals, 12-13

of sp^2 orbitals, 13

of sp^3 orbitals, 13-14

Bond lengths, and bond orders, 53-54

Bonding orbitals, 36-38

Bond orders, p_{ij}, of benzene, 54

of bicyclobutadiene, 124-125

and bond lengths, 54-55

of 1,3-butadiene, 54

calculation of, 53-54

check on calculations of E_π with, 55

definition of, 53

and free valence index, 56-57

of small-ring hydrocarbons and radicals, 128-130

1,3-Butadiene, approximate calculation of E_π of, 110

  atomic orbital model of, 19–20

  bond distances of, 53

  bond orders of, 53

  charge distribution calculated for, 59

  energy levels of, 43–46

  free valence indexes of, 57

  frontier–electron treatment of, 96–97

  group theory applied to, 61–63

  LCAO treatment of, 43–52

  molecular diagram of, 59

  self–consistent field of, 59

C_2 character table, 71
C_2 operations, 64–65, 70–71
Carbanions, small–ring types of, 129–130
Carbon, electronic configuration, 4, 5

  hybridization of, 15

  overlap integrals for, 29–30

  promotion energy of, 15

  resonance integral for, 34
Carbonium ions, calculations of energy of, 87–89

  reactivity of, 87, 100–101

  small–ring types of, 129–130
Character tables, C_2, 71

  D_{2v}, 66
Charge distributions, q_i, of benzyl cation and anion, 106

  of bicyclobutadiene, 125

  of 1, 3–butadiene, 59

  definition of, 58

  in diazoazide configurations, 139

  for pyrrole, 80

  and reactivity, 94–95
Chemical reactivity (see Reactivity)

148

Coefficients of wave functions, for bicyclobutadiene, 122–124
    calculation of, 34, 49–51, 122–124
Configuration interaction, 116
Correlation, electron, 117
Coulomb integrals, α, for carbonium ions, 101
    correction for nonself-consistent fields, 60
    definition of, 31
    in reactivity problems, 92, 95
Crossing of energy profiles, 93, 103
Cyclobutadiene, degenerate orbitals of, 74
    dipositive ion of, 74
    energy levels and electronic configuration of, 73
    substituted types of, 128–130
Cyclooctatetraene, atomic orbital model of, 21
    nonplanar structure of, 21, 86
Cyclopentadienyl anions, 76
Cyclopentadienyl radical, group theory applied to, 70–71
Cyclopropenium cations, 76, 129

d-Orbitals, 78
DE$_\pi$ (see Resonance energy)
Degeneracy, accidental, 4
Degenerate orbitals, 4
    of cyclobutadiene, 74–75
    properties of, 74–75
7-Dehydronorbornyl cation, calculation of energy of, 87
Delocalization procedures for calculation of reactivities, 100–101
Diazoazides, 77
    cyclization of, 131–139
    LCAO treatment of configuration of, 131
Diels–Alder reaction, 102–103
Di-p-xylylene, free valence index of, 58

E_π, approximate calculations of, 110–112

 of benzyl radical, 106

 calculation of, for benzenediazonium ion, 134–135

  of bicyclobutadiene, 120–121

  from bond orders, 55

  for butadiene, 43–46

  of diazoazide configurations, 131–139

  for ethylene, 42

  of organic azides, 135–136

 of cyclobutadiene, 73

 of various radicals, 111

Electron correlation, 117

Electron pairs, 4

Electron probability, 2

Electron spin, 4

Electronic charges (see Charge distribution)

Electronic configurations of atoms, 7

Electronic energy, sample calculations for H_3, 118–120

Electrons, unpaired, 4

Ethylene, atomic orbital model of, 18

 free valence index of, 58

 LCAO treatment of, 42–43

 localized bonds of, 41–42, 43

 wave functions of, 42

Exclusion principle, 4, 23

$\mathscr{F}_i$ (see Free valence index)

4n + 2 Rule, 75–76, 127–130

Free radical reactivity, frontier electron methods for, 97

Free radicals, E_π values for, 111

 small-ring types of, 129–130

  (see also Benzyl radical)

Free radical reactivity, free valence index and, 57-58, 94-96

Free valence index, $\mathfrak{F}_i$, of bicyclobutadiene, 125

  from bond orders, 56-57

  of 1,3-butadiene, 57

  definition of, 56

  and reactivity, 57-58, 94, 96

  of small-ring hydrocarbons and radicals, 128-130

  of trimethylenemethane, 56, 58

  for typical substances, 58

Frontier-electron method, 96-97

Frontier orbital, 97

Ground state predictions of reactivity, 94

Group theory, cyclopentadienyl radical determinant and, 70

  naphthalene determinant and, 64-70

  simplification of determinants with 61-72

    (see also Symmetry operations)

H_3, calculation of binding energy of, 118-120

Hamiltonian energy operator, 24

Heteroatoms, Coulomb integrals for, 78-79

  LCAO treatment of molecules with, 77-80

  resonance integrals for, 78

Heterocyclic molecules, LCAO treatment of, 77-80

Hexaazabenzene, 77

Homoallyl cations, 87-89

Hückel's rule, 75-76, 127-130

Hund's rule, 4, 6, 73

Hybridization, 11-14

  in acetylene, 17-18

  in benzene, 20-21

  in ethylene, 18-19

  in molecules with unshared pairs, 14-15

Hydrogen, electronic configuration and energy of, 39–40
Hydrogen atom, 2–3
Hydrogen molecule ion, energy levels and wave functions for
       33–36
Hydrogen sulfide, bond angles of, 11

Identity operation, 64
Interelectronic repulsion, 4, 39–40, 115
    and configuration interaction, 116

Kopineck's tables, 83–84

LCAO method, definition of, 25–26
LCAO treatment, of benzenediazonium ion, 134–135
    of bicyclobutadiene, 120–126
    of butadiene, 43–52
    of diazoazide configurations, 131–139
    of ethylene, 42–43
    of H_3, 118–120
    of hydrogen molecule, 39–40
    of hydrogen molecule ion, 35–37
    of organic azides, 135–136
    of small-ring hydrocarbons and radicals, 127–130
    validity of, 104, 115
Localization procedures, 98–100
    approximate method for, 113–114
Localized bonds, 40–41

Methyl radical, free-valence index of, 58
Mobile bond order (see Bond order)
Molecular diagrams, of azulene, 94
    of bicyclobutadiene, 126
    of small-ring hydrocarbons and radicals, 129
    of 1, 3-butadiene, 59

Molecular orbitals, concept of, 25–26
Multiple bonds, orbitals for, 15–19

NAH (see Nonalternant hydrocarbons)
Naphthalene, approximate calculation of substitution in, 113–114
    approximate calculation of E_π of, 113
    calculated bond distances of, 54–55
    group theory applied to, 64–70
NBMO (see Nonbonding molecular orbitals)
Nitrogen, atomic orbital model for, 16
    Coulomb and resonance integrals for, 78
    LCAO treatment of diazoazide configurations, 131–139
    organic azides, 135–136
    promotion energy of, 15
Nodes, in butadiene wave functions, 52
    in molecular wave functions, 38
Nonalternant hydrocarbons, definition and examples of, 60
Nonbonding molecular orbitals, of benzyl radical, 105–107
    calculation of coefficients for, 107–109
    for calculation of localization energies, 113–114
    of cyclobutadiene, 74
    definition of, 74
    E_π from, 110
Nonorthogonal wave functions, 29
Nonplanar systems, 82–90
Nonself-consistent fields, 59–60, 115
    heteroatoms and, 79
Normalization factor, 35
Normalized wave functions 24–25, 35
Nucleophilic reactivity, 97

Orbital hybridization, 11-14
Orbitals, antibonding, 36-38
    atomic, 2-4
    bonding, 36-38
    degenerate, 4
    hydrogen-like, 1-4
    nonbonding, 74, 105-107
    overlap of, 6, 9
    p, 3
        bond formation with, 8
    s, 2-3
        bond formation with, 8
Orientation in aromatic substitution, 91-100
    calculation of, 113-114
Orthogonal wave functions, 29
Overlap, in benzene 20, 21
    in cyclooctatetraene, 21
    of hybrid orbitals, 14
    of s and p orbitals, 9
    of sp orbitals, 12
    of sp^2 orbitals, 13
    of sp^3 orbitals, 14
Overlap integral, calculation of, 82-85
    for bent bonds, 88-89
    for carbon as a function of hybridization and distance, 29-30
    definition of, 28-29
    of nonplanar p orbitals, 82-85
Oxygen, Coulomb and resonance integrals for, 78

p Bonds, angles of, 8-11
p Orbitals, calculation of overlap of, 82-85
    π overlap of, 16
p_{ij} (see Bond order)
Pauli exclusion principle, 4, 23

Pentalene, approximate calculation of E_π of, 112

Pentazoles (see Diazoazides)

π Bonds, 16

    in acetylene, 17

    in benzene, 20–21

    in butadiene, 20

    in ethylene, 18

    in nitrogen, 17

π–Electron energy (see E_π)

π–Overlap, 16

Product stabilities, and reactivity, 102–103

Propyl chloride, reactivity of, 100–101

Pseudoaromatic compounds, 128–129

Pyridine, LCAO treatment of, 78

Pyrrole, charge distributions calculated for, 80

q_i (see Charge distribution)

Radicals (see Free radicals)

Rate problems (see Reactivity)

Reaction rates (see Reactivity)

Reactivity, approximate calculations of, 113–114

    aromatic substitution, 113–114

    of azulene, 94

    carbonium ion, 87, 100–101

    and charge distributions, 94–95

    delocalization procedure for calculation of, 100–101

    in Diels–Alder reaction, 102–103

    and free valence index, 95

    LCAO treatment of, 88–89, 91–104

    localization procedure for calculation of, 98–100

    perturbation methods for, 95–98

    problems of, 91–93, 104

Resonance energy, of benzene, 48
  of benzyl radical, 106
  of bicyclobutadiene, 121
  of 1,3-butadiene, 47
  of cyclobutadiene, 73
  of small-ring hydrocarbons and radicals, 128-130
Resonance integral, calculation as function of distance, 82
  carbon, as a function of distance, 33
  definition of, 32
  as function of angle, 32
  and overlap integral, 82

S_{ij} (see Overlap integral)
Secular determinant, 28
Self-consistent fields, definition of, 59
σ Bonds, 6
σ-π interactions, 115
Single bonds, 6
Singlet state, 74, 127-130
sp^3-Bonds, in acetylene, 17-18
sp-Orbitals, 12-13
sp^2-Orbitals, 13
sp^3-Orbitals, 13-14
Symmetry operations, D_{2v} symmetry, 63-66
  two-fold axes, 63-66, 70-71

Tetraazacyclobutadiene, 77
Transition state, 92-93
Trimethylene methane, free valence indexes of, 56, 58
Triphenylmethyl chlorides, ionization of, 101
Triple bond, atomic orbitals for, 16-18
Triplet state, 128-130
  of cyclobutadiene, 73

Tropylium cations, 76

Unshared electron pairs, bond formation of atoms with, 14-15

Variation method, 27-28
    and configuration interaction, 116

Wave equation, 23-25
Wave functions, of bicyclobutadiene, 121-124
    of 1,3-butadiene, 48-52
    derivation through group theory, 67-69, 71
    of ethylene, 42
    for hydrogen molecule ion, 34-35
    normalized, 24-25
Water, atomic orbital model of, 9, 10
    bond angles in, 9-11
    hybridization in, 14-15